Hall AS "Teaching Coriolis' Law" Proc ASEE Vol. 55, 1947-48, p. 757

KINEMATICS AND LINKAGE DESIGN

Kinematics and Linkage Design

ALLEN S. HALL, JR.

Professor of Mechanical Engineering

Purdue University

PRENTICE-HALL, INC., Englewood Cliffs, N. J. 1961

Library of Congress Catalog Card Number 61-7431
Printed in the United States of America 51529C

PREFACE

Approximately twelve years ago at Purdue University, at the suggestion and with the encouragement of Professor E. S. Ault, the author introduced a course in Kinematics as an elective for seniors and beginning graduate students, whose purpose was to follow up the conventional analysis and descriptive work of the undergradute Mechanisms course with concepts and techniques (some new, some quite old but at that time much ignored in this country) of importance in a logical approach to the kinematic design of mechanisms. This book is an outgrowth of the class notes developed for that course. It is planned as a *text* for a one-semester three-credit-hour course. It does not claim to be a comprehensive reference compendium, but rather an *introduction* to kinematic design. Some familiarity with motion analysis of mechanisms is presumed, but even this could be supplied within the three-credit-hour framework by cutting back a bit on some of the other material.

A full catalogue of the author's debts would be impossible to prepare. In addition to people and sources specifically acknowledged in the text, the following were especially helpful:

Professor Allan C. Dunk taught for one semester from a manuscript copy of the text, helping to catch errors and points needing clarification.

Through their writings (in addition to those listed in the bibliography) and through personal association, Dr. Rudolph Beyer and Ing. Kurt Hain have had considerable influence on the author's thinking.

C. W. Allen, E. E. Hahn and R. Aronson, while graduate students, were generous with their time in computer programming and problem checking.

The magazines *Machine Design* (Penton Publishing Company), *Design News* (Rogers Publishing Company) and *Product Engineering* (McGraw-Hill) regularly describe new mechanisms and new applications for old devices. Some of these have suggested illustrations and problems.

ALLEN S. HALL, JR.

CONTENTS

Chapter 2 Review of Velocity and Acceleration Analysis in Plane Motion (cont.)

KINEMATICS AND LINKAGE DESIGN

1

Introduction. 4-bar mechanisms

1.1 *Kinematic design*

The kinematic design of a mechanism involves two major steps:

(1) The selection of the *type* of mechanism to be used

(2) The determination of suitable *dimensions*

Step (1), at present, must be considered a part of the *art* of engineering. The designer must rely largely on his own ingenuity, on past experience (his own and that of others as reported in the technical literature and patent descriptions), and on his understanding of the principles governing the combination of mechanical elements to produce kinematic chains having the requisite number of degrees of freedom.

Step (2) is more susceptible of a scientific approach and has been the object of much activity, accelerated in recent years by increased need for more accurately designed mechanisms capable of performing new functions and of doing old jobs at higher and higher speeds. The availability of large-capacity digital computers has encouraged designers to set up accurate solutions for problems previously solved roughly by trial procedures.

This book is restricted primarily to a consideration of some of the theory and techniques useful in step (2). Most of the theory discussed will be general for plane motion, but design examples will be limited to lower-paired plane mechanisms or their equivalents.

1.2 *Equivalent 4-bar mechanisms and the 4-bar mechanism as an element in more complex mechanisms*

Much of the theory of machine kinematics has been developed for the 4-bar mechanism (4 links, 4 pin joints). There are several reasons for this emphasis.

(1) The 4-bar mechanism is widely used. It is the simplest possible lower-paired plane mechanism.

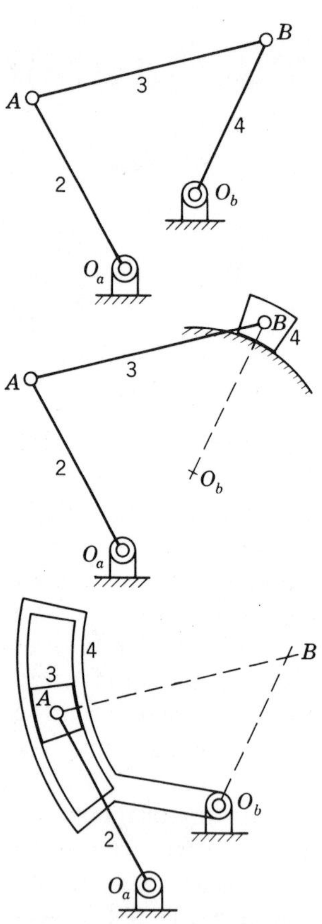

Fig. 1.1 Kinematically identical mechanisms having the 4-bar as the basic skeleton. Differences are only in the physical forms of some links.

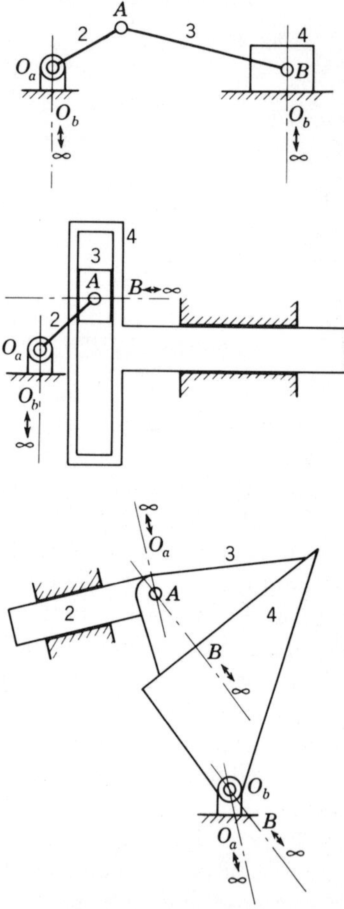

Fig. 1.2 Examples of 4-link mechanisms in which the basic 4-bar skeleton contains one or more infinitely long links.

(2) Many mechanisms whose physical forms are not that of the 4-bar have 4-bars for their basic skeletons, hence theory developed for the 4-bar applies to them.
(3) Many mechanisms which are not 4-bars are equivalent to 4-bars in some aspects of their motions. As far as these motions are concerned, 4-bar theory is applicable.
(4) Several important more complex mechanisms have 4-bars as elements; theory of the 4-bar is therefore useful in the design of these mechanisms.

In order to make maximum use of our knowledge of the 4-bar mechanism, we should learn to recognize it where it occurs as the basic skeleton, as an equivalent mechanism, or as part of a more complex mechanism. Figures 1.1–1.5 show examples of each situation.

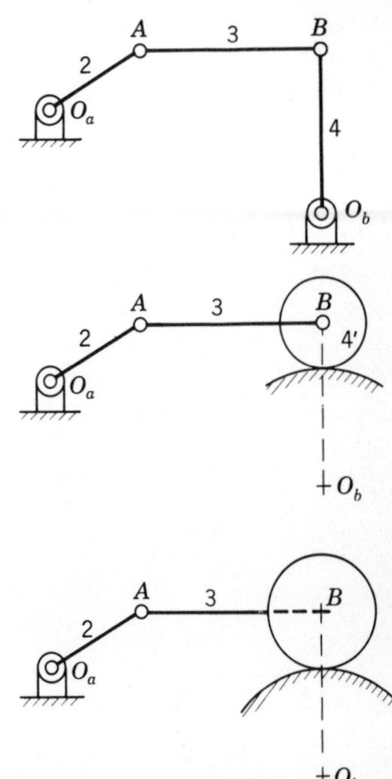

Fig. 1.3 Mechanisms that are equivalent as far as the motion of link 3 is concerned.

1.3 *Applications of the 4-bar mechanism*

The 4-bar mechanism and its equivalents appear in some of the oldest as well as the most modern machines, in small instruments and some of the heaviest mechanical equipment

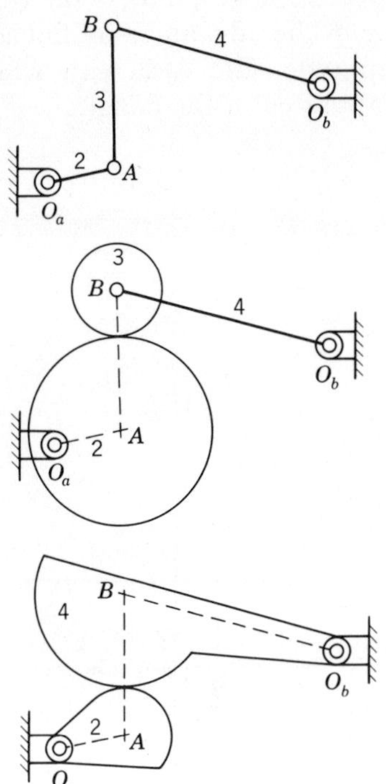

Fig. 1.4 Mechanisms that are equivalent in the relative motions of links 2 and 4.

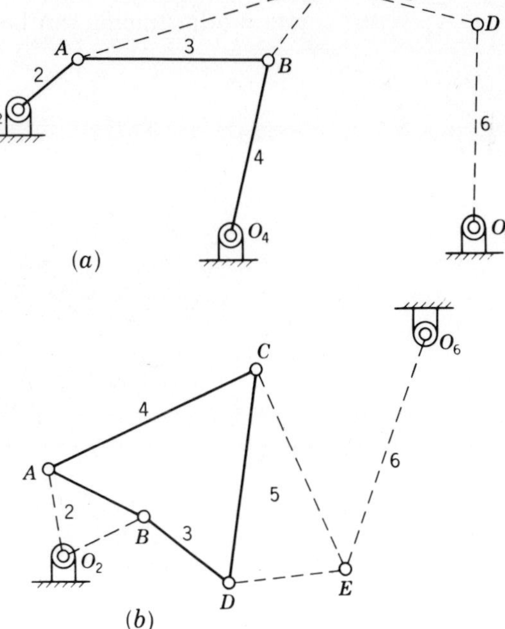

Fig. 1.5 Useful 6-link mechanisms of which the 4-bar is an important element.

made. The functions performed defy classification except in a very general way, such as (a) guiding, (b) converting or transforming motions, (c) providing mechanical advantage, etc.

Current technical literature continually carries descriptions of new machines. One of the best ways to build up a background of ideas for the possible uses of different mechanisms (not just the 4-bar) is to study these publications. The following articles provide a beginning by describing a few 4-bar applications. The figures accompanying these descriptions are not intended to be dimensionally accurate but are to be regarded as sketches conveying the general idea of the application.

1.4 *Lawn-sprinkler oscillator, Fig. 1.6*

One of the most common uses for the 4-bar mechanism is the conversion of rotary to oscillatory motion. In the lawn sprinkler of Fig. 1.6 the 4-bar drive mechanism causes the sprinkler tube to oscillate about a horizontal axis. Crank 2 is rotated by a small water-operated motor. Links 4, 4′, and the sprinkler tube oscillate as one rigid body about an axis through O_4 perpendicular to the paper. The angle of oscillation can be changed by clamping 4′ in a different angular position with respect to 4, thus changing the effective length, O_4B, of the 4-bar output lever. This illustrates one of the advantages of linkage-type mechanisms over the cam type—the ease with which certain adjustments can be incorporated in the design.

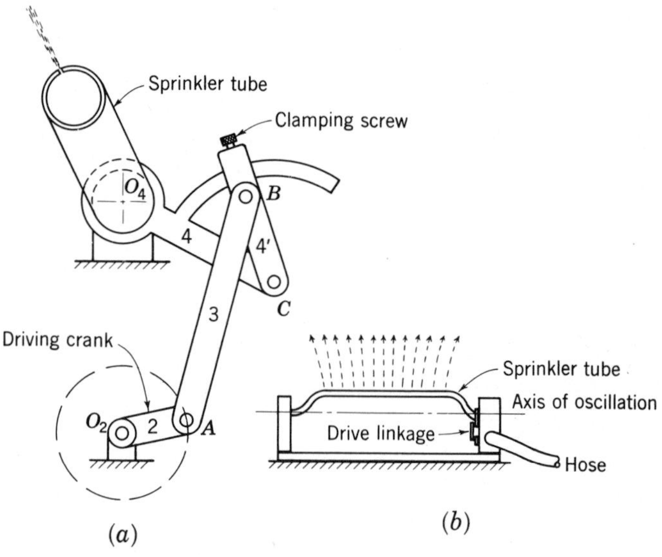

Fig. 1.6 Application of the 4-bar mechanism in a lawn-sprinkler oscillator.

1.5 *Auto-hood hinge linkage, Fig. 1.7*

On most automobiles the hood does not pivot on a simple hinge but is guided by a linkage so that, when the hood is raised, the rear edge of the hood is moved forward a short distance. Many of these hinges are 4-bar mechanisms, of which the one in Fig. 1.7 is typical. Variations in the proportions of the links and the placing of the spring will be found in different makes and models of automobiles.

In addition to designing the linkage to guide the hood as desired, there is the interesting problem of determining a suitable spring characteristic and the points of attachment. The spring is usually so designed and placed that it approximately counterbalances the weight of the hood in the middle range of its motion. When the hood is up the spring overcounterbalances, and when the hood is down the spring undercounterbalances.

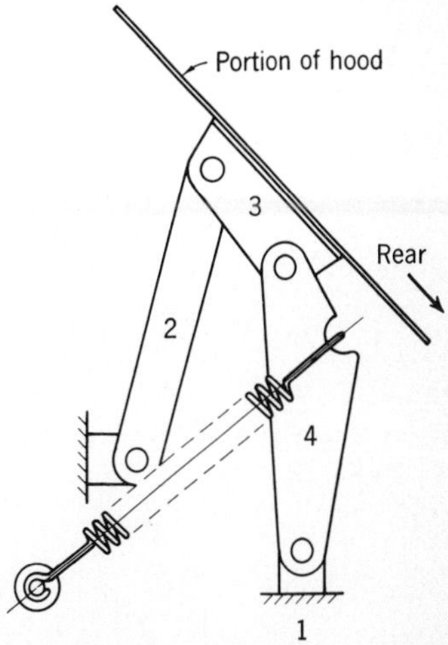

Fig. 1.7 4-bar hinge linkage for auto hood.

1.6 *Fork-lift truck, Fig. 1.8*

In this application the 4-bar mechanism serves to guide the lifting forks upward and back at a slight angle, in nearly a straight line. This design eliminates the mast used in many lift trucks, providing for maneuverability of the truck in areas of low headroom.

The kinematic design problem would be to determine

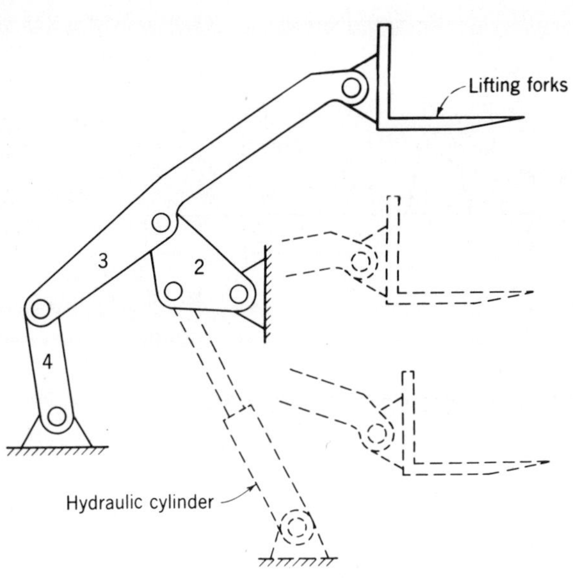

Fig. 1.8 Mechanism of fork-lift truck without mast.

dimensions of the 4-bar skeleton such that point C would have the desired approximate straight-line path over the required range of motion. The solution would have to satisfy other requirements to fit in with the over-all design of the complete machine. For example, there would be limitations on the possible locations of pivots O_2 and O_3.

1.7 *Web cutter, Fig. 1.9*

This is an interesting solution to the problem of cutting a continuously moving web or strip of material (paper, cloth, sheet metal, etc.) into sheets. The blades of the shears are attached, one to an extension of the connecting rod (or "coupler"), link 3, the other to the oscillating lever (or "rocker"), link 4. As the driving crank rotates, the relative angular motion between links 3 and 4 creates the "scissors" action to cut the web. During the cutting portion of the motion cycle the horizontal velocity of the blades must very nearly match the web velocity.

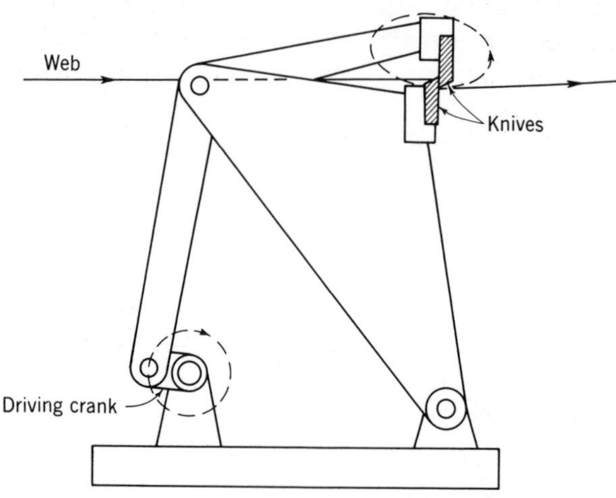

Fig. 1.9 Web cutter.

1.8 *Guide for truing diamond, Fig. 1.10*

The parallelogram form of the 4-bar mechanism has found many applications for its special properties. In this example links 2 and 3 are the cranks of a parallelogram 4-bar provided with two connecting rods, links 4 and 5. Link 6, pin-jointed to the two connecting rods, exactly duplicates the

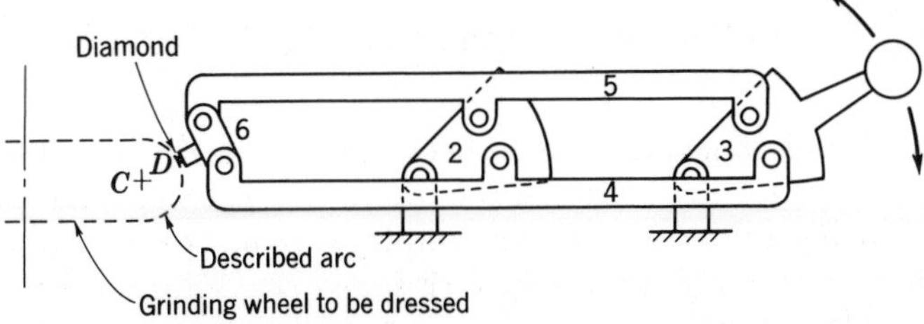

Fig. 1.10 Parallelogram 4-bar used to guide a truing diamond in dressing a grinding wheel.

motions of the cranks, moving around point C as though pivoted there. Thus the truing diamond is guided on a circle arc to dress a grinding wheel to the radius CD. The radius can be changed by changing the location of the diamond on link 6.

1.9 *Typewriter linkage, Fig.* 1.11

An examination of the different typewriters on the market will reveal a great variety in the linkages activating the type bars. However, most of them use one or more 4-bar mechanisms as essential elements in the linkage. Figure 1.11 shows a typical example. Depressing the key (not shown) causes rod 7 to move to the left, turning cranks 6 and 4 counterclockwise and type bar 2 clockwise. An important feature of the design is that the proportions of the 4-bar mechanism made up of links 1, 4, 3, and 2 are such that the angular velocity ratio ω_2/ω_4 becomes large as the type bar approaches the striking position.

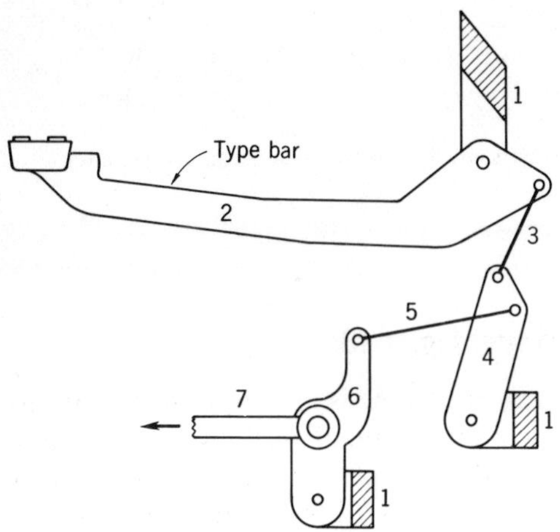

Fig. 1.11 A typewriter linkage. Two 4-bar mechanisms in series.

1.10 *Toy-walking mechanism, Fig.* 1.12

Much ingenuity has been displayed in developing mechanisms for toys. One of the interesting problems has been the devising of a realistic, yet simple, walking mechanism for mechanical toy animals. Fig. 1.12 shows one solution that has been widely used.

Crank 2 is driven by a conventional spring motor and gear train. The rear leg (link 5) of the toy is pivoted on the frame and caused to oscillate. Crank 2, frame 1, connecting rod 4, and rear leg 5 form one 4-bar mechanism.

The foreleg, link 3, is given a more complicated motion. The upper end of the leg is slotted and guided by a pin fixed to the frame. A point on the forefoot is thus given a roughly elliptical path.

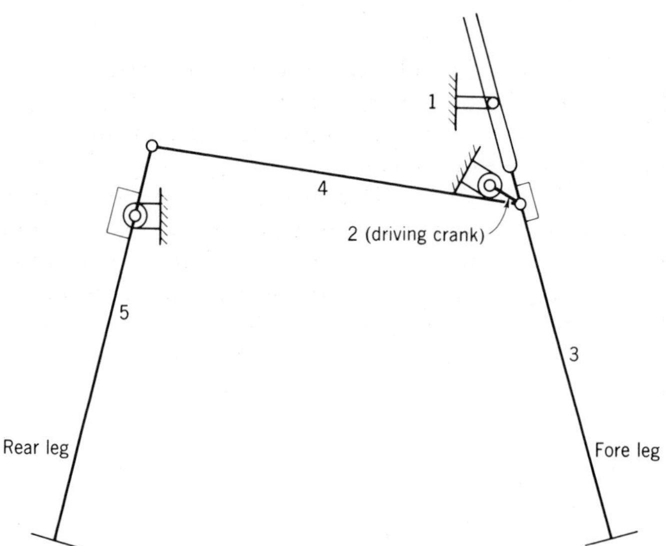

Fig. 1.12 A toy-walking mechanism. Two 4-bar mechanisms in parallel.

1.11 *A computing linkage, Fig.* 1.13

The term "computing linkage" is used to describe applications (usually in instruments and control mechanisms) in which a variable y linearly correlated with the motion of the output link and a variable x linearly correlated with the motion of the input link bear some desired functional relation to each other. The linkage is said to "compute" $y = f(x)$.

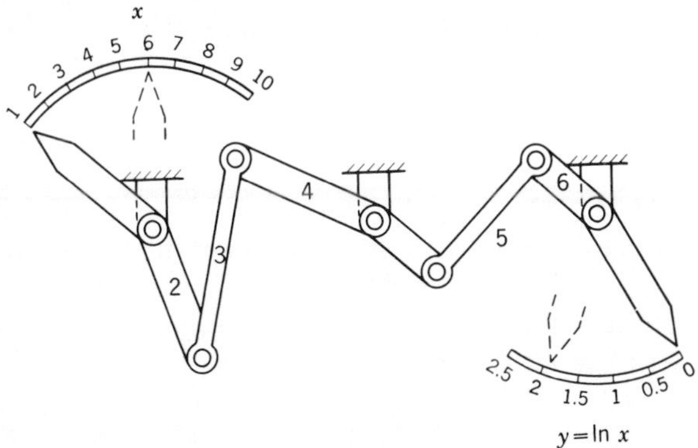

Fig. 1.13 A computing linkage composed of two 4-bar mechanisms in series.

Figure 1.13 shows a mechanism consisting of two 4-bars in series designed to compute $y = \ln x$ in the range $1 < x < 10$. The input and output cranks are shown provided with pointers and scales. Usually this is not done, since a computing linkage is not ordinarily used as a slide-rule substitute but rather is a device performing some mechanical function such as, for example, adjusting a valve opening in response to a pressure variation in accordance with some desired functional relation between the two.

1.12 *Inertia starter, Fig. 1.14*

This 4-bar mechanism is used in the train between an engine and a rotating mass used to supply the energy for starting. The output crank is connected, through step-up gearing, to the starter pinion of the engine. The input crank can be connected by a jaw clutch to a shaft turned by the rotating mass.

To start the engine, the 4-bar is placed in "initial" position with the jaw clutch disengaged. The rotating mass is brought up to speed, either by hand crank or electric motor. The jaw clutch is then engaged, and the 4-bar driven to "final" position. Substantially shockless transfer of kinetic energy from the rotating mass to the engine is accomplished. As the input crank rotates 180 deg. from initial to final position, the output crank also turns 180 deg. The key feature of the design is that the 4-bar mechanism is so proportioned that the angular velocity ratio of input to output crank varies from infinity to zero during the operating period.

In inertia starters using a friction clutch to connect the rotating mass to the engine, a large part of the kinetic energy of the rotating mass is necessarily dissipated in friction at the clutch faces. This design avoids that energy loss.

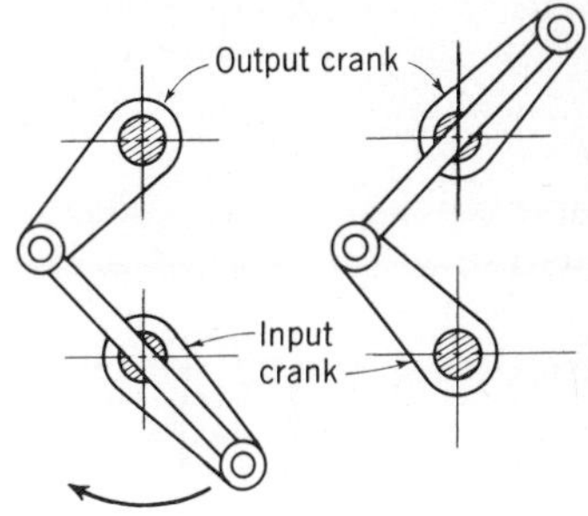

Fig. 1.14 The 4-bar mechanism used in the train of a unique inertia starter for engines.

1.13 *Adjustable lead-screw tapper, Fig. 1.15*

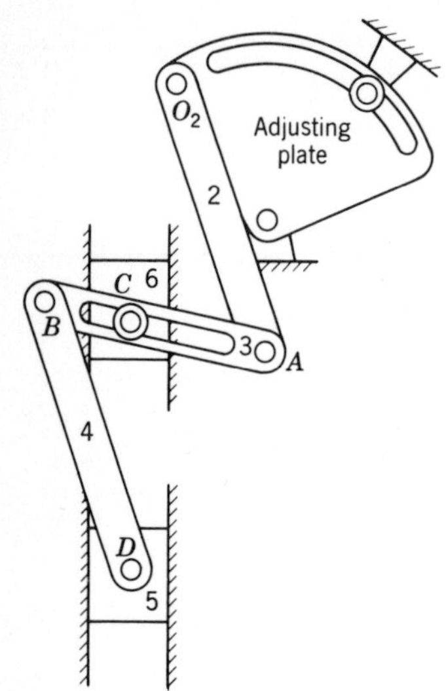

Fig. 1.15 Adjustable lead-screw tapper.

In this device a lead screw drives slide 6, and a tap is carried by slide 5. The linkage magnifies the motion of slide 5 as compared to 6 so that a single lead screw serves to feed taps of different leads. Adjustments to accommodate different tap leads include (1) shifting fixed pivot O_2 by means of the adjusting plate, (2) shifting the location of pin C along link 3, and (3) (not indicated by the sketch) changing the length of link 3.

1.14 *Deep-drawing press, Fig. 1.16*

The sketch shows the skeleton form of a mechanism used on a deep-drawing press. Pinion P drives through compound gears G_1 and G_2 to gears G_4 and G_3 on shafts of cranks 2 and 3 respectively. Cranks 2 and 3 thus rotate clockwise at the same speed. The design produces a fairly uniform velocity during the working portion of the down stroke of the ram (link 7) plus a quick-return action.

Special attention is called to that part of the mechanism composed of the frame (link 1), the two cranks (links 2 and 3), and the two rods (links 4 and 5). These parts alone comprise a 5-bar, two-degree-of-freedom linkage. It is constrained (one degree of freedom removed) by the presence of the gearing, which forces cranks 2 and 3 to rotate in a fixed ratio. With this ratio equal to $+1$, as it is in this example, it can be shown that the motion of point C is identical with that of a point on the coupler of a certain 4-bar mechanism. Thus we have here the equivalent, in one sense, of a 4-bar mechanism. This kind of equivalence will be discussed in Chapter 4.

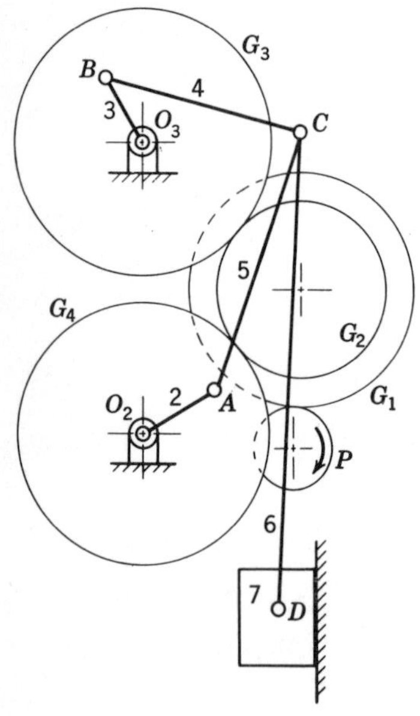

Fig. 1.16 Mechanism of a deep-drawing press.

Problems and Exercises

E1.1 For the web cutter described in Art. 1.7 and shown in Fig. 1.9, suggest adjustments which might be provided in order that sheets of different lengths may be cut. Explain your suggestions with the help of sketches.

E1.2 Sketch and describe briefly any applications of the parallelogram 4-bar mechanism with which you may be familiar.

E1.3 In the toy-walking mechanism of Fig. 1.12, links 1, 2, and 3 form the equivalent of a 4-bar mechanism. Explain exactly what this equivalence is. Sketch the equivalent 4-bar.

E1.4 Examine mechanical toys for different action mechanisms. Make sketches and write brief explanations of at least three different mechanisms found in toys.

E1.5 The adjustable lead-screw tapper mechanism shown in Fig. 1.15 is a 6-link mechanism having some links of infinite length. It is a particular example of the general form shown in Fig. 1.5(a). Identify corresponding links in the two figures.

E1.6 Start a notebook for sketches, clippings, and descriptions of interesting mechanisms. Periodically look through technical journals and commercial publications for examples.

E7.7 Examine auto-hood hinge linkages for (a) variations of the type shown in Fig. 1.7 and (b) types which are not 4-bar mechanisms. Get approximate dimensions and make sketches.

E1.8 Examine at least two different typewriters. Sketch the type-bar operating mechanisms.

2

Review of velocity and acceleration analysis in plane motion

2.1 *Introduction*

The most widely taught procedure for analysis of velocities and accelerations in mechanisms is the "polygon" or "image" method. This involves the writing of "relative" velocity and acceleration vector equations and their graphical solutions. Important relations will be summarized here, without proofs, and illustrated by application to several problems. For a more detailed treatment see any text on the kinematics of machines.

2.2 *Notation*

The symbols to be used in this discussion are defined as follows:

A, B, C, etc. .... points, or particles.

1, 2, 3, etc.	rigid bodies, links of the mechanism. Numeral 1 will ordinarily designate the fixed link of a mechanism.
A_2, B_5, etc.	the numeral subscript indicates the body or link to which the point belongs. Used where this is not clear from the drawing, or to distinguish between coincident points belonging to different bodies.
OA, CD, etc.	the length of the directed line segment from the first to the second point. (Note that $OA = -AO$.)
V	linear velocity.
V_a, V_b, etc.	velocity of the point referred to by the subscript, measured in a coordinate system attached to the fixed link of the mechanism, unless stated otherwise.
$+\!\!\!\rightarrow$ $\rightarrow$	vector addition, vector subtraction.
V_{ba}	velocity of B relative to A. By definition V_{ba} will equal $V_b \rightarrow V_a$. (This use of the word *relative* is not universally accepted. However, no confusion should arise so long as the only meaning we attach to the word is that given by the above definition.)
ω	angular velocity.
ω_2, ω_5, etc.	angular velocity of the body indicated by the subscript, measured in a coordinate system attached to the fixed link of the mechanism unless stated otherwise.
ω_{52}	angular velocity of 5 relative to 2. For plane motion $\omega_{52} = \omega_5 - \omega_2$
A	linear acceleration.
A_a, A_b, etc.	acceleration of the point indicated by the subscript, measured in a coordinate system attached to the fixed link of the mechanism unless stated otherwise.
A_{ba}	acceleration of B relative to A. By definition A_{ba} will equal $A_b \rightarrow A_a$. (See note under V_{ba}.)
A_a^n, A_{ba}^n	the superscript n indicates that component which is perpendicular to the corresponding velocity. For example, A_{ba}^n is that component of A_{ba} which is perpendicular to V_{ba}. Read A_{ba}^n "the normal acceleration of B relative to A."
A_a^t, A_{ba}^t	the superscript t indicates that component which is parallel to the corresponding velocity. Read A_{ba}^t "the tangential acceleration of B relative to A."
α	angular acceleration, $d\omega/dt$.
α_2, α_4, etc.	angular acceleration of the body indicated by the subscript, measured in a coordinate system attached to the fixed link of the mechanism unless stated otherwise.
α_{42}	angular acceleration of 4 relative to 2. For plane motion, $\alpha_{42} = \alpha_4 - \alpha_2$.

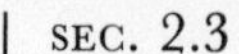

2.3 *Two points belonging to the same rigid body, Fig. 2.1*

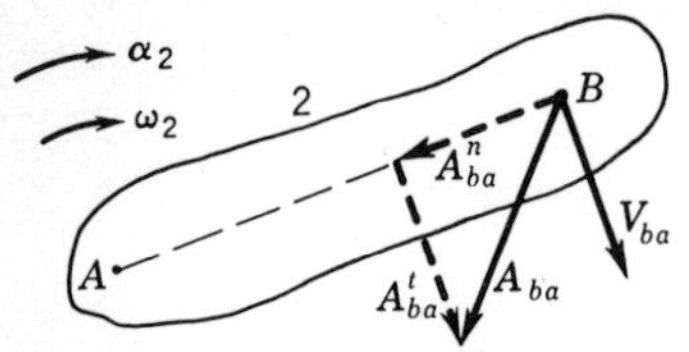

Fig. 2.1 Relative velocity and acceleration for two points belonging to the same rigid body.

Let A and B be two points belonging to body 2. Then

$$V_{ba} = (AB)\omega_2$$

and

$$A_{ba} = A^n_{ba} \leftrightarrow A^t_{ba}$$

where $A^n_{ba} = (AB)\omega_2^2$ (or V^2_{ba}/AB or $V_{ba}\,\omega_2$) directed from B toward A.

$A^t_{ba} = (AB)\alpha_2$ directed perpendicular to AB and in the sense obtained by rotating AB 90 deg. in the sense of α_2.

If one of the two points has zero velocity, the velocity of the second relative to the first equals the absolute velocity of the second. See Fig. 2.2.

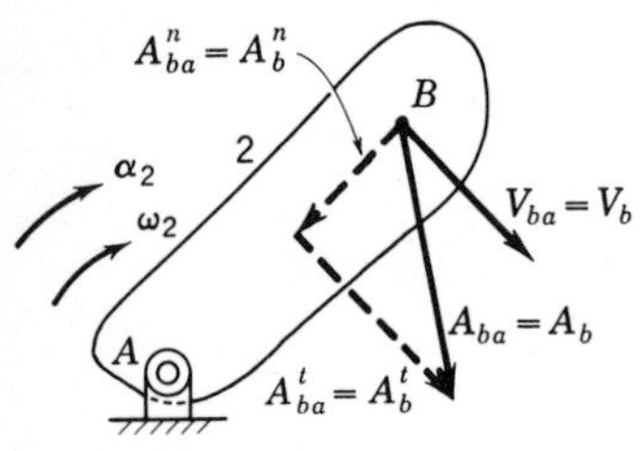

Fig. 2.2 Relative velocity and acceleration become absolute velocity and acceleration when the reference point has zero velocity and acceleration.

$$V_{ba} = V_b - V_a = V_b$$

when $V_a = 0$. Also, for accelerations

$$A_{ba} = A_b - A_a = A_b$$

when $A_a = 0$. One of these conditions may exist without the other, as illustrated in Fig. 2.3. Here V_a equals zero, but A_a does not equal zero, so $V_{ba} = V_b$, but $A_{ba} \neq A_b$.

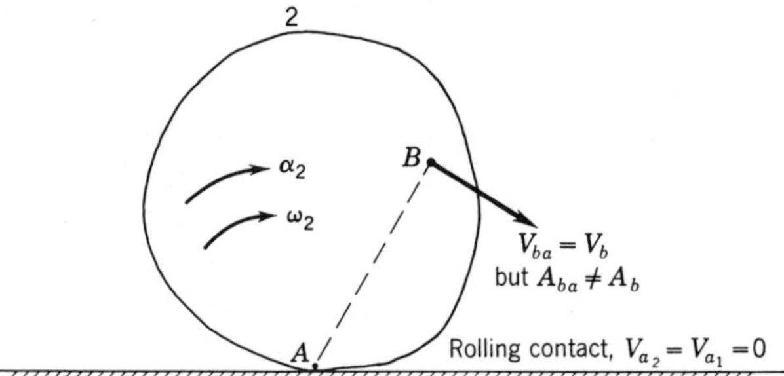

Fig. 2.3 Point A_2 has zero velocity but not zero acceleration. It can not be treated as a fixed pivot in acceleration calculations.

2.4 *Two coincident points belonging to different bodies: velocity, Fig. 2.4*

Two points, P_2 and P_3, belonging, respectively, to bodies 2 and 3 and, at the instant, coincident in location at point P of the motion plane, have a relative velocity directed along the tangent to the path which one of the points traces on the body containing the other point. The path which P_2 traces on 3 and the path which P_3 traces on 2 are tangent at P. If the coincident points under consideration are also the physical contact points for the two bodies, as in Fig. 2.5, the common tangent to the relative paths is also the common tangent to the body outlines at P.

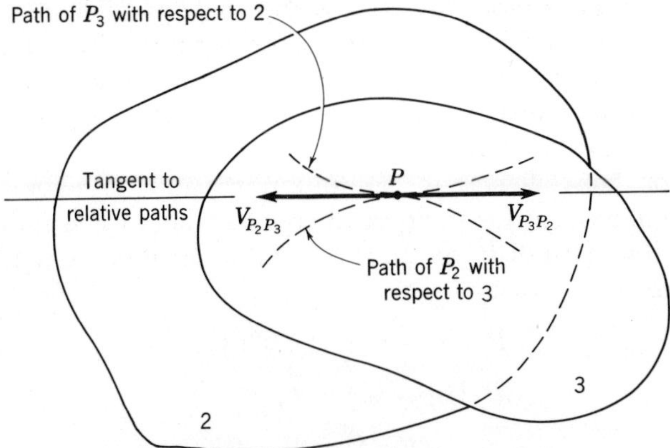

Fig. 2.4 Relative velocities of coincident points belonging to different bodies.

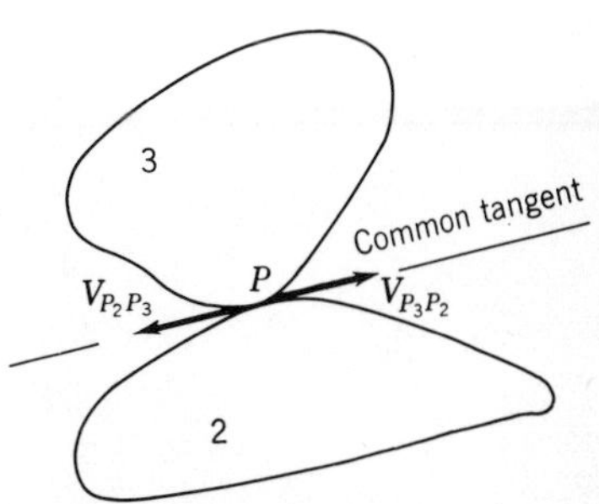

Fig. 2.5 Coincident points at the point of physical contact between two bodies.

2.5 *Two coincident points belonging to different bodies: acceleration, Fig. 2.6*

In discussing the relative acceleration $A_{p_3p_2}$ it is helpful to visualize an extra link X pin-jointed to body 3 at P and to body 2 at C, where C is the instantaneous center of curvature of the path traced by P_3 on (with respect to) body 2. Such a link would have angular velocity ω_x and angular acceleration α_x. The relative acceleration between P_3 and P_2 may be expressed as follows:

$$A_{p_3p_2} = A^n_{p_3p_2} \leftrightarrow A^t_{p_3p_2}$$

where $$A^t_{p_3p_2} = (CP)\,(\alpha_x - \alpha_2) = (CP)\,\alpha_{x2}$$

and $$A^n_{p_3p_2} = (CP)\,(\omega_x^2 - \omega_2^2)$$

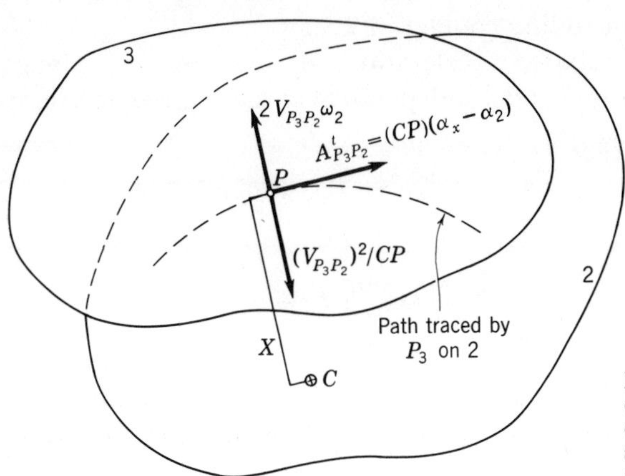

Fig. 2.6 Components of the relative acceleration $A_{p_3p_2}$. C is the center of curvature of the path traced by P_3 on (with respect to) body 2. X is an extra link imagined to be pinned between C_2 and P_3.

The tangential component $A^t_{p_3p_2}$ is directed parallel to $V_{p_3p_2}$ (perpendicular to CP) and in the sense obtained by rotating CP 90 deg. in the sense of α_{x2}. The normal component $A^n_{p_3p_2}$ is directed parallel to CP and in the sense of CP if ω_2 exceeds ω_x, in the opposite sense if ω_x exceeds ω_2.

For convenience in computations and to avoid an indeterminate form for the special case in which CP is infinite (straight-line path of P_3 on 2), it is usual to express the normal component as follows:

$$A^n_{p_3p_2} = (CP)(\omega_x - \omega_2)^2 + 2(CP)(\omega_x - \omega_2)\omega_2$$

however $$(CP)(\omega_x - \omega_2) = V_{p_3p_2}$$

so $$A^n_{p_3p_2} = [(V_{p_3p_2})^2/CP] + 2V_{p_3p_2}\omega_2$$

The first component on the right of this expression is frequently called the "relative normal" acceleration and in some texts is represented by the symbol $a^n_{p_3p_2}$ to distinguish it from the total normal component which we have called $A^n_{p_3p_2}$. The second component is known as the "Coriolis" component or the "compound supplementary" acceleration. Rules for sense are as follows:

$(V_{p_3p_2})^2/CP$ is directed from P toward C.

$2(V_{p_3p_2})\omega_2$ has the sense obtained by rotating the $V_{p_3p_2}$ vector 90 deg. in the sense of ω_2.

2.6 *Rolling contact: relative acceleration at point of contact, Fig. 2.7*

Consider two bodies in plane relative motion and having rolling contact at point P. Let C be the center of curvature of body 2 and B the center of curvature of body 3, corresponding to the point of contact, P.

By definition the relative velocity, $V_{p_3p_2}$, is zero if the bodies are in rolling contact at P.

The relative acceleration, $A_{p_3p_2}$, is directed along the common normal and is independent of the angular accelerations of the bodies.

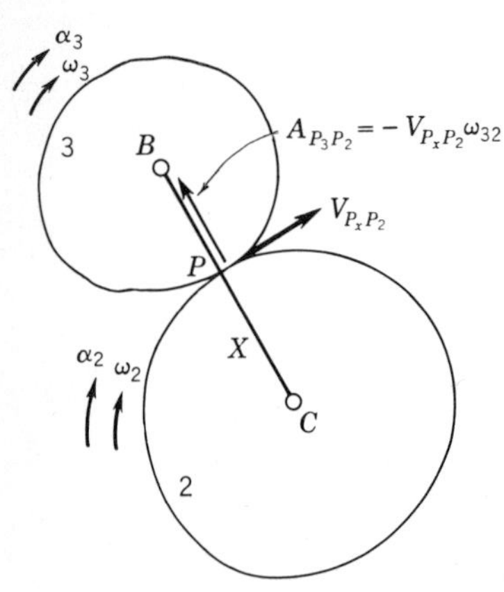

Fig. 2.7 Figure for derivation of rolling contact acceleration relation.

$$A_{p_3p_2} = A^n_{c_2p_2} + A^n_{b_3c_2} + A^n_{p_3b_3}$$

where $$A^n_{c_2p_2} = (V_{c_2p_2})^2/PC$$

$$A^n_{b_3c_2} = (V_{b_3c_2})^2/CB$$

$$A^n_{p_3b_3} = (V_{p_3b_3})^2/BP$$

If we visualize an extra link, X, pin-jointed to body 2 at C and to body 3 at B, then the following shorter relation can be written

$$A_{p_3p_2} = -V_{p_xp_2}\omega_{32}$$

If body 2 were fixed, the relations would become

$$A_{p_3} = A^n_{b_3} + A^n_{p_3b_3} = -V_{p_x}\omega_3$$

The significance of the negative sign in the above expressions is that the sense of $A_{p_3p_2}$ (or A_{p_3}) is the sense obtained by rotating the $V_{p_xp_2}$ (or V_{p_x}) vector 90 deg. *opposite* the sense of ω_{32} (or ω_3).

2.7 *Approaching a problem*

The previous articles outline the essential relations for velocity and acceleration analysis of any plane mechanism by the polygon method. Knowledge of these relations is necessary, but not sufficient, for successfully solving problems.

It is not possible to give a rigidly detailed outline of procedure applicable to all problems. The general plan is to start with whatever velocity and acceleration data are given and then to work through the mechanism by way of a series of points A, B, C, D, etc., solving equations of the form

$$V_b = V_a \nrightarrow V_{ba} \qquad A_b = A_a \nrightarrow A_{ba}$$

$$V_c = V_b \nrightarrow V_{cb} \qquad A_c = A_b \nrightarrow A_{cb}$$

$$V_d = V_c \nrightarrow V_{dc} \qquad A_d = A_c \nrightarrow A_{dc}, \text{ etc.}$$

The key to success is the proper choice of points to deal with at each step of the solution. In general, the choice must be such that all *normal* acceleration components can be calculated. This means that all *distances* needed in the calculations must be determinable by inspection of the drawing. For example, suppose that at one step of a solution we propose to go from a point P_3 to the coincident point P_4, solving the vector equation

$$A_{p_4} = A_{p_3} \nrightarrow A_{p_4p_3}$$

To calculate a part of the normal component of $A_{p_4p_3}$ we need to know the radius of curvature of the path which P_4 traces on link 3. If this radius cannot be determined by inspection of the mechanism, we should change our attack. It will be found helpful to keep the following ideas in mind:

(1) The points used need not fall within the physical outlines of the links. Each link may be considered extended indefinitely in any direction.

(2) If two links are joined by a lower pair (surface contact at the joint), the path which *any* point belonging to one of the links traces on the other is a circle arc with its center on the axis of the joint. (See Fig. 2.8).

(3) If two links are joined by a higher pair (point contact in the plane of motion), the point belonging to one

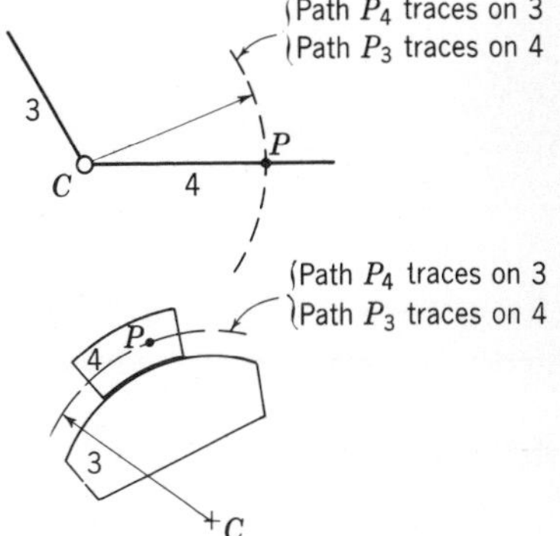

Fig. 2.8 Lower-pair joints. The path which *any* point belonging to one link traces on the other is a circle arc with its center on the axis of the joint.

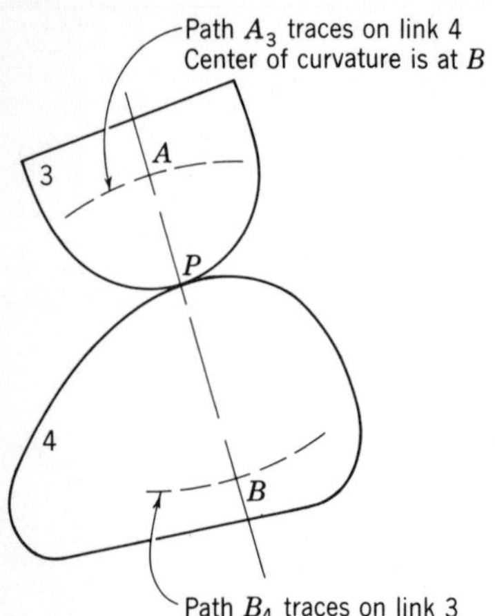

Fig. 2.9 Higher-pair joint. The only relative path centers of curvature which can be determined by inspection are for the paths traced by A_3 on 4 and B_4 on 3. A and B are the centers of curvature of the bodies corresponding to the point of contact P.

link at its center of curvature (corresponding to the point of contact) traces on the second link a path whose center of curvature coincides with the center of curvature of the second link. (See Fig. 2.9).

(4) For the purpose of velocity and acceleration analysis it is always permissible to visualize an extra link pinned between the centers of curvature of two bodies in direct contact (higher pairing).

In the following articles a number of examples will be analyzed to illustrate possible approaches and procedures in different situations.

2.8 *Problem: velocity and acceleration analysis of a linkage-gear mechanism*

The mechanism shown in Fig. 2.10 consists of the 4-bar mechanism 1, 2, 3, 4, plus a gear 5. A portion of link 3 is in the form of a gear meshing with 5. The axes of oscillation of 4 and 5 are colinear but 4 and 5 are not directly connected in any way. The mechanism is driven by crank 2 rotating at a constant speed of ω_2, clockwise. Our problem is to determine the angular velocity and angular acceleration of gear 5 for the position of crank 2 shown.

VELOCITY ANALYSIS

(1) Calculate the velocity of A.

$$V_a = (O_2A)\omega_2$$

(2) Solve for the velocity of B.

$$V_b = V_a \mapsto V_{ba}$$

V_{ba} is perpendicular to AB.

V_b is perpendicular to O_4B.

(3) Solve these equations simultaneously for the velocity of P_3.

$$V_{p_3} = V_a \mapsto V_{p_3a}$$
$$V_{p_3} = V_b \mapsto V_{p_3b}$$

V_{p_3a} is perpendicular to AP.

V_{p_3b} is perpendicular to BP.

The graphical solution of the above equations for V_b and V_{p_3} results in the velocity polygon of Fig. 2.10. All absolute velocity vectors are drawn radiating from the pole point O_v and labeled with appropriate lower-case letters at their tips. Vector O_va represents V_a, O_vb represents V_b, ab represents V_{ba}, etc.

(4) Since the pitch circles of the two gears are in rolling contact at P, $V_{p_5} = V_{p_3}$.

(5) Calculate the angular velocity of gear 5.

$$\omega_5 = V_{p_5}/O_5P$$

A slightly different procedure for determining ω_5 would be as follows, after step (2) above:

(3′) Calculate the angular velocity of link 3.

$$\omega_3 = V_{ba}/AB$$

(4′) Calculate the angular velocity of link 4.

$$\omega_4 = V_b/O_4B$$

(5′) Calculate the angular velocity of 3 relative to 4.

$$\omega_{34} = \omega_3 - \omega_4$$

(6′) The angular velocity of 5 relative to 4 is

$$\omega_{54} = \omega_{34}(BP/O_5P)$$

(7′) The angular velocity of 5 is then

$$\omega_5 = \omega_4 + \omega_{54}$$

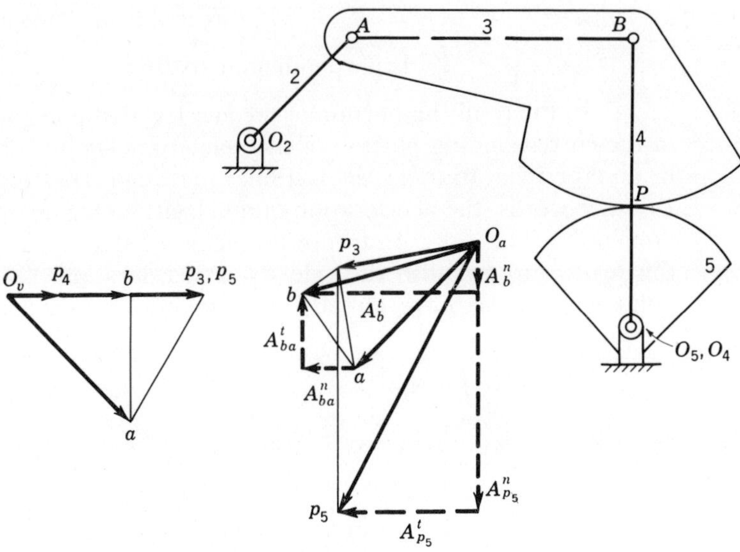

Fig. 2.10 Velocity and acceleration analysis of a linkage-gear mechanism.

ACCELERATION ANALYSIS

(1) Calculate the acceleration of point A.

$A_a = A^n_a = (O_2A)\omega_2^2$, directed from A toward O_2.

(2) Solve for the acceleration of point B.

$$A_b = A_a \leftrightarrow A^n_{ba} \leftrightarrow A^t_{ba}$$

$$A_b = A^n_b \leftrightarrow A^t_b$$

$A^n_{ba} = (V_{ba})^2/AB$ (calculate), directed from B toward A.

A^t_{ba} is perpendicular to AB.

$A^n_b = (V_b)^2/O_4B$ (calculate), directed from B toward O_4.

A^t_b is perpendicular to O_4B.

The graphical solution of the above equations for A_b forms a part of the acceleration polygon in Fig. 2.10. The pole point for the polygon is O_a. Vector O_aa represents A_a, O_ab represents A_b, etc.

(3) Solve simultaneously the following two equations for A_{p_3}.

$$A_{p_3} = A_a \leftrightarrow A^n_{p_3a} \leftrightarrow A^t_{p_3a}$$

$$A_{p_3} = A_b \leftrightarrow A^n_{p_3b} \leftrightarrow A^t_{p_3b}$$

$A^n_{p_3a} = (V_{p_3a})^2/AP$, directed from P toward A.

$A^t_{p_3a}$ is perpendicular to AP.

$A^n_{p_3b} = (V_{p_3b})^2/BP$, directed from P toward B.

$A^t_{p_3b}$ is perpendicular to BP.

In the resulting portion of the acceleration polygon (and in the corresponding portion of the velocity polygon) it should be observed that triangle abp_3 is similar to triangle ABP of link 3. In other words, the acceleration and velocity polygons contain "images" of the links. In future problems we shall make use of this feature to establish the velocity or acceleration of a third point when these have already been found for two points of the same link.

(4) Solve for A_{p_5}.

$$A_{p_5} = A_{p_3} \leftrightarrow A_{p_5p_3}$$

$$A_{p_5} = A^n_{p_5} \leftrightarrow A^t_{p_5}$$

$A_{p_5p_3}$ is directed along line O_5PB.

(This is the rolling contact situation discussed in Art. 2.6.)

$A^n_{p_5} = (V_{p_5})^2/O_5P$ directed from P toward O_5.

$A^t_{p_5}$ is perpendicular to O_5P.

(5) Calculate the angular acceleration of 5.

$$\alpha_5 = A^t_{p_5}/O_5P$$

An alternate way to find α_5 would be to proceed as follows, after step (2) above:

(3′) Calculate $\alpha_3 = A^t_{ba}/AB$

(4′) Calculate $\alpha_4 = A^t_b/O_4B$

(5′) The angular acceleration of 3 relative to 4 is

$$\alpha_{34} = \alpha_3 - \alpha_4$$

(6′) The angular acceleration of 5 relative to 4 is then

$$\alpha_{54} = \alpha_{34}(BP/O_5P)$$

(7′) Finally

$$\alpha_5 = \alpha_4 + \alpha_{54}$$

2.9 *Problem: velocity and acceleration analysis of a cam mechanism*

In the cam mechanism of Fig. 2.11 the angular acceleration of the roller is to be determined for a constant cam angular velocity, ω_2. Point C locates the center of curvature of that portion of the cam profile in contact with the roller at the instant under consideration.

Several procedures, differing in some details, might be used on this problem. Two will be outlined.

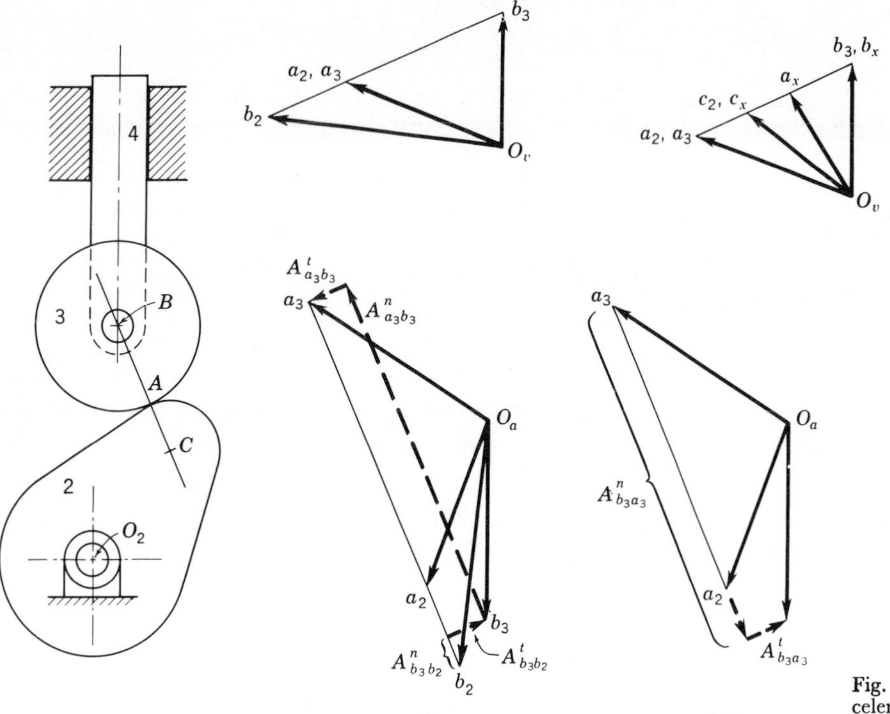

Fig. 2.11 Velocity and acceleration analyses of a cam mechanism. Two solutions.

FIRST SOLUTION

(1) Calculate $V_{b_2} = (O_2B)\omega_2$

and $V_{a_2} = (O_2A)\omega_2$

Note that $V_{a_3} = V_{a_2}$ (rolling contact).

(2) Solve $V_{b_3} = V_{b_2} \leftrightarrow V_{b_3b_2}$

$V_{b_3b_2}$ is directed tangent to the path traced by B_3 on link 2. This path is an arc with C as center. Hence $V_{b_3b_2}$ is perpendicular to line CB.

(3) Calculate $A_{b_2} = A^n_{b_2} = (O_2B)\omega_2^2$

and $A_{a_2} = A^n_{a_2} = (O_2A)\omega^2$

(4) Solve $A_{b_3} = A_{b_2} \leftrightarrow A^n_{b_3b_2} \leftrightarrow A^t_{b_3b_2}$

where $A^n_{b_3b_2} = (V_{b_3b_2})^2/CB + 2V_{b_3b_2}\omega_2$

(See Art. 2.5.)

(5) Solve simultaneously

$$A_{a_3} = A_{b_3} \leftrightarrow A^n_{a_3b_2} \leftrightarrow A^t_{a_3b_3}$$

$$A_{a_3} = A_{a_2} \leftrightarrow A_{a_3a_2}$$

(6) Calculate $\alpha_3 = A^t_{a_3b_3}/BA$

The velocity and acceleration polygons for this solution are shown in Fig. 2.11(b).

SECOND SOLUTION

(1) Imagine an extra link, X, pin-jointed to 2 at C and to 3 at B.

Calculate $V_{cx} = V_{c_2} = (O_2C)\omega_2$

and $V_{a_3} = V_{a_2} = (O_2A)\omega_2$

(2) Solve $V_{bx} = V_{b_3} = V_{cx} \leftrightarrow V_{bxcx}$

(3) Solve for V_{ax} by image

$$V_{axcx}/V_{bxcx} = (CA)/(CB)$$

(4) Calculate $A_{a_2} = A^n_{a_2} = (O_2A)\omega_2^2$

(5) Calculate $\omega_3 = V_{b_3a_3}/AB$

and $\omega_{32} = \omega_3 - \omega_2$

(6) Solve $A_{a_3} = A_{a_2} \leftrightarrow A_{a_3a_2}$

where $A_{a_3a_2} = -V_{axa_2}\omega_{32}$

(7) Solve $A_{b_3} = A_{a_3} \leftrightarrow A^n_{b_3a_3} \leftrightarrow A^t_{b_3a_3}$

(8) Calculate $\alpha_3 = A^t_{b_3a_3}/AB$

The velocity and acceleration polygons for this solution are shown in Fig. 2.11(c).

2.10 *Problem: velocity and acceleration analysis using an "auxiliary point"*

The use of so-called "auxiliary points" is helpful in some situations. An auxiliary point is any point other than the obvious ones (pin centers, contact points, centers of curvature of contacting bodies, etc.) whose use will expedite the solution of the problem. Reference (1)* is a good source for more detail on the subject. Here we shall illustrate the use of an auxiliary point in one example.

The mechanism shown in Fig. 2.12 is driven by link 2 turning at constant speed, ω_2. We are required to determine the angular velocity and angular acceleration of link 4.

VELOCITY ANALYSIS

(1) Calculate $V_{b_2} = (O_2B)\omega_2$

and $V_e = (O_2E)\omega_2$

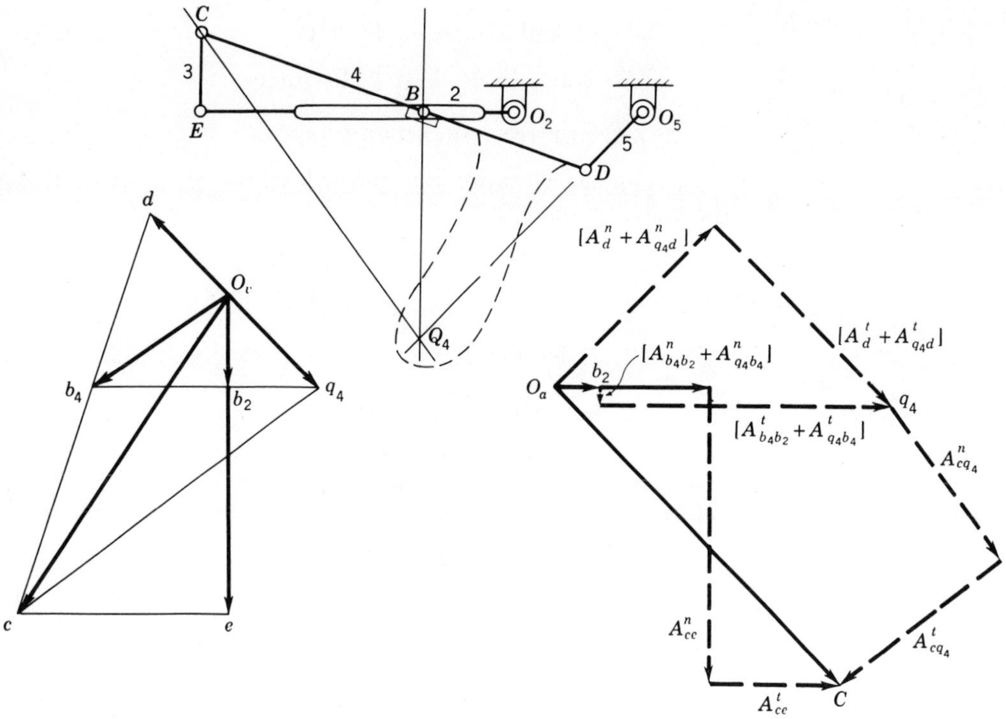

Fig. 2.12 Velocity and acceleration analysis using an "auxiliary point."

*References are listed at the back of book; see page 155 ff.

It might seem, at first glance, that the next step might be to solve either of the following:

$$V_{b_4} = V_{b_2} \leftrightarrow V_{b_4 b_2}$$
$$V_c = V_e \leftrightarrow V_{ce}$$

However, we quickly see there are too many unknowns in both equations since the directions of V_{b_4} and V_c are not known. Searching for another point, belonging to link 4, whose velocity *can* be determined, we try Q_4, located as shown in the figure.

(2) Solve for V_{q_4}

$$V_{q_4} = V_{b_2} \leftrightarrow (V_{b_4 b_2} + V_{q_4 b_4})$$
$$V_{q_4} = (V_d + V_{q_4 d})$$

Since $V_{b_4 b_2}$ and $V_{q_4 b_4}$ are parallel, they may be treated as a single vector of known direction. V_d and $V_{q_4 d}$ are also parallel and may be treated as a single vector of known direction. Thus the two equations can be solved simultaneously for V_{q_4}. The location of Q_4 was chosen to make things work out this way.

(3) Solve for V_c

$$V_c = V_{q_4} \leftrightarrow V_{cq_4}$$
$$V_c = V_e \leftrightarrow V_{ce}$$

(4) Calculate $\omega_4 = V_{cq_4}/QC$

(5) Solve for V_{b_4} and V_d by image

ACCELERATION ANALYSIS

The acceleration analysis will follow the same outline as the velocity analysis.

(1) Calculate $A_{b_2} = A^n_{b_2} = (O_2B)\omega_2^2$

$$A_e = A^n_e = (O_2E)\omega_2^2$$

(2) Solve for A_{q_4}

$$A_{q_4} = A_{b_2} \leftrightarrow A_{b_4 b_2} \leftrightarrow A_{q_4 b_4}$$
$$= A_{b_2} \leftrightarrow (A^n_{b_4 b_2} + A^n_{q_4 b_4}) \leftrightarrow (A^t_{b_4 b_2} + A^t_{q_4 b_4})$$
$$A_{q_4} = A_d \leftrightarrow A_{q_4 d}$$
$$= (A^n_d + A^n_{q_4 d}) \leftrightarrow (A^t_d + A^t_{q_4 d})$$
$$A^n_{b_4 b_2} = 2V_{b_4 b_2}\omega_2$$

(The path traced by B_4 on link 2 is a straight line, so the $a^n_{b_4 b_2}$ part of $A^n_{b_4 b_2}$ is zero.)

$$A^n_{q_4 b_4} = (V_{q_4 b_4})^2/BQ$$

$(A^t_{b_4 b_2} + A^t_{q_4 b_4})$ is perpendicular to BQ.

$$A^n_d = (V_d)^2/O_5D$$

$$A^n_{q_4d} = (V_{q_4d})^2/DQ$$

$(A^t_d + A^t_{q_4d})$ is perpendicular to OD_5Q.

(3) Solve for A_c

$$A_c = A_{q_4} \mapsto A^n_{cq_4} \mapsto A^t_{cq_4}$$

$$A_c = A_e \mapsto A^n_{ce} \mapsto A^t_{ce}$$

(4) Calculate $\alpha_4 = A^t_{cq_4}/QC$

2.11 *Time- and labor-saving techniques*

A velocity or acceleration analysis for a single position of a mechanism ordinarily yields too little information to be of much use to the designer. Usually such analyses are required for a number of positions throughout a full cycle of operation. This means a certain amount of tedious, repetitive work in the contruction of the polygons, even though the general procedure of solution, when once mapped out for one mechanism position, applies to all others. The routine labor of the analysis can be materially reduced by following the suggestions listed below.

(1) Draw the mechanism in all the positions to be analyzed. It is not necessary to fill in all lines in all positions, but through a systematic numbering and lettering scheme all key points (pin centers, etc.) should be clearly located.

(2) Construct the velocity polygons for all positions.

   (a) Make the pole point for the velocity polygons coincide with the pivot of the driving link.

   (b) Instead of drawing the velocity vectors in their true directions, draw them all turned 90 deg. opposite the sense of rotation of the driving link.

   (c) Make the velocity scale equal to the product of the drawing scale and the angular velocity of the driving link.

$$K_v = K_s\omega$$

   K_s stands for the number of length units represented by 1 in. on the drawing.

   K_v stands for the number of velocity units represented by 1 in. of velocity vector.

   ω represents the angular velocity of the driving link, in radians/unit time.

(3) Construct the acceleration polygons for all mechanism positions.

(a) Make the pole point for the acceleration polygons coincide with the pivot of the driving link.
(b) Instead of drawing acceleration vectors in their true directions, draw them reversed.
(c) Make the acceleration scale equal to the product of the drawing scale and the square of the angular velocity of the driving link.

$$K_a = K_s \omega^2$$

K_a stands for the number of acceleration units represented by 1 in. of acceleration vector.

2.12 *Quick construction for 4-bar acceleration analysis*

The suggestions of the previous article have been applied to the 4-bar mechanism of Fig. 2.13, in which the input is crank 2 rotating at constant speed. The turned velocity polygon is O_2AB', in which

O_2A represents V_a

O_2B' represents V_b

and AB' represents V_{ba}

In the turned acceleration polygon

O_2A represents A_a $(=A_a^n)$

AB'' represents A_{ba}^n

and O_2B''' represents A_b^n.

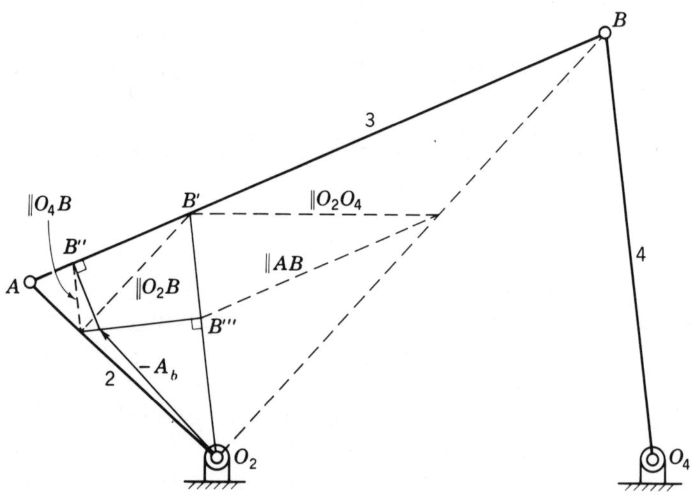

Fig. 2.13 Short acceleration construction for the 4-bar mechanism.

The broken lines in the layout are construction lines used to determine the lengths AB'' and O_2B''' in place of calculating A^n_{ba} and A^n_b. In the analysis of any mechanism it is possible to devise relatively simple graphical means for determining the lengths of normal acceleration vectors if the previous suggestions are followed. It is left as an exercise for the student to prove that the construction shown in Fig. 2.13 does correctly determine the vector lengths for A^n_{ba} and A^n_b, and hence that the acceleration polygon displayed is correct.

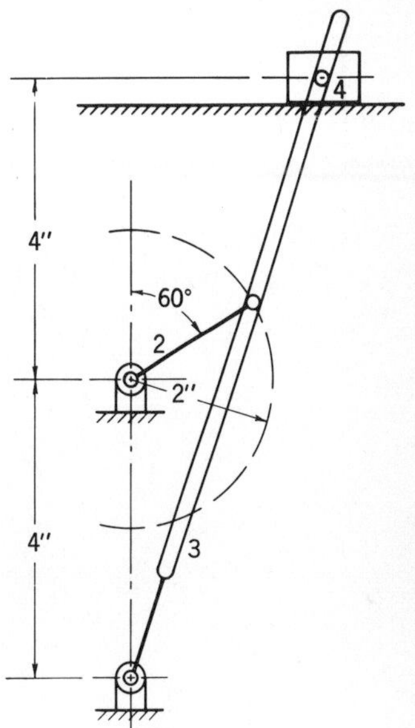

Fig. 2.14 Mechanism for problems E2.1 and E2.6.

Problems and Exercises

E2.1 In the mechanism of Fig. 2.14 assume an angular velocity $\omega_2 = 20$ rad. ps (radians per second) clockwise, constant. Determine the acceleration of slider 4.

E2.2 In the mechanism of Fig. 2.15 the velocity of slider 2 is 10 fps and the acceleration is 200 fps², both toward the right. Determine the angular acceleration of link 4.

E2.3 For the mechanism of Fig. 2.16 assume the crank to be rotating clockwise with a constant angular velocity of 100 rad. ps. Determine (a) the angular acceleration of gear 4 and (b) the angular acceleration of rack 3.

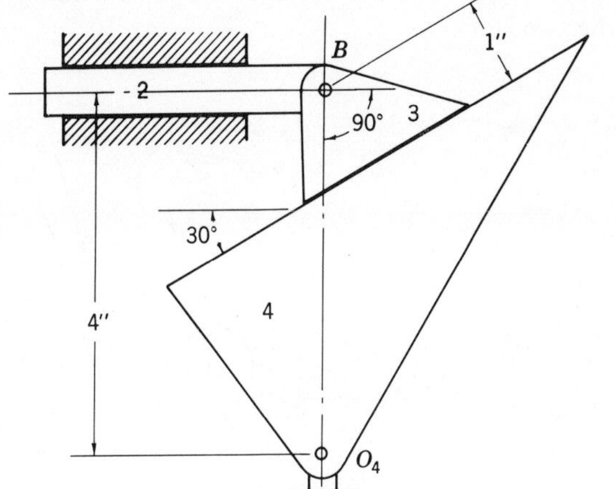

Fig. 2.15 Mechanism for problem E2.2.

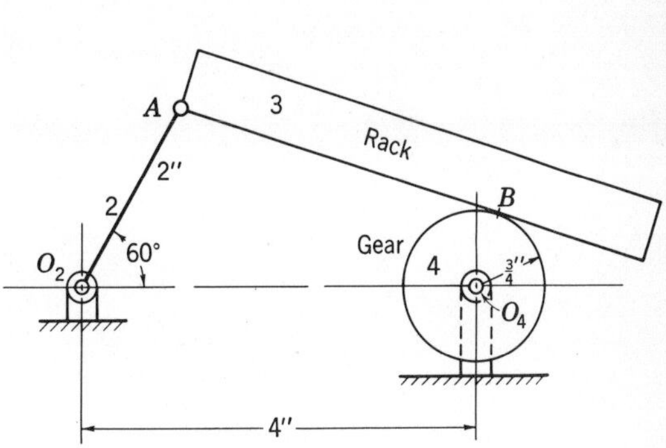

Fig. 2.16 Mechanism for problem E2.3.

E2.4 Prove that the construction shown in Fig. 2.13 does correctly determine A_b, as stated in Art. 2.12.

E2.5 How should the construction shown in Fig. 2.13 be modified for the situation in which the angular acceleration of crank 2 is not zero?

E2.6 Develop a simplified construction for determining the acceleration of slider 4 in the mechanism of Fig. 2.14.

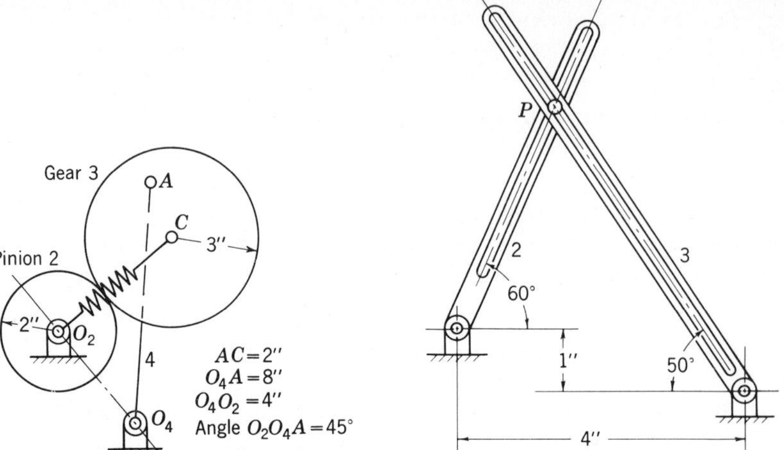

Fig. 2.17 Mechanism for problem E2.7. Fig. 2.18 Mechanism for problem E2.8.

E2.7 For the mechanism of Fig. 2.17 assume pinion 2 to be turning clockwise with a constant angular velocity of 100 rad. ps. Determine the angular accelerations of gear 3 and link 4.

E2.8 Slotted links 2 and 3 in Fig. 2.18 are independently driven at angular velocities of 30 and 20 rad. ps clockwise and have angular accelerations of 900 and 400 rad. ps^2 clockwise, respectively. Determine the acceleration of *P*, the center of the pin carried at the intersection of the two slots.

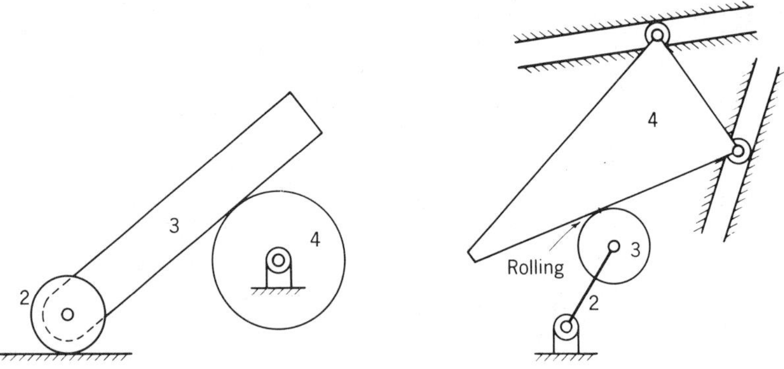

Fig. 2.19 Mechanism for problem E2.9. Fig. 2.20 Mechanism for problem E2.10.

E2.9 In the mechanism of Fig. 2.19 wheel 2 rolls to the right with a constant angular velocity. Link 3 is maintained in rolling contact with link 4. Outline in detail a procedure for determining the angular acceleration of link 3.

E2.10 Outline in detail a procedure for determining the acceleration of any point belonging to link 4 in the mechanism of Fig. 2.20. Assume the angular velocity and angular acceleration of crank 2 to be known.

3

Gross motions in the 4-bar mechanism

3.1 *Classes of 4-bar chains*

All 4-bar kinematic chains can be divided into two classes, distinguished from each other by differences in the possible relative motions of the links.

Class I

In all members of this class the shortest link can make a full revolution relative to each of the others. The three longer links can only oscillate relative to each other.

Class II

In all members of this class no link can make a full revolution relative to any other.

To which class a particular chain belongs can be determined quickly by noting certain inequalities in link lengths. Harding (2) has suggested a notation which makes the discussion of these inequalities relatively simple and easy to remember. Refer to Fig. 3.1. The notation is as follows:

$$a + b > c + d$$
$$a > b$$
$$c > d$$

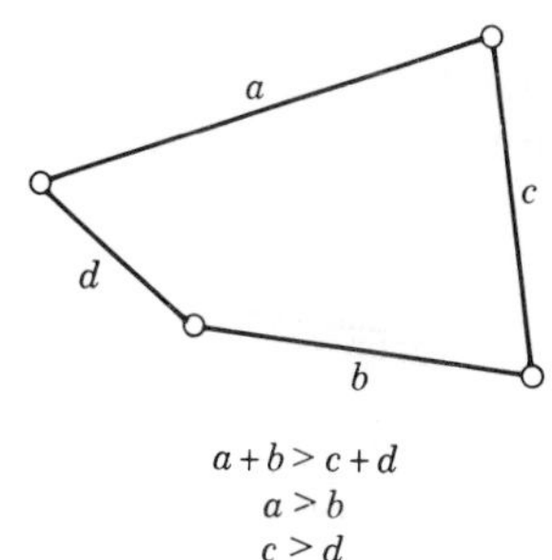

Fig. 3.1 Notation used in discussing classification of 4-bar chains.

Of that pair of opposite links having the greater length sum we label the longer link a and the shorter link b. The letters are the link "names" as well as indications of the link lengths. Of the other pair of opposite links we label the longer c and the shorter d.

Having established the notation, we can state the relations which characterize class I and class II chains.

For class I chains

$$a - b < c - d$$

For class II chains

$$a - b > c - d$$

Fig. 3.2 shows an example of each.

Numerous subclasses and borderline cases can be distinguished for which one or more of the inequalities stated above becomes an equality. For example, if $a + b = c + d$ and $a - b = c - d$, then $a = c$ and $b = d$, which yields the "isosceles" chain in Fig. 3.3.

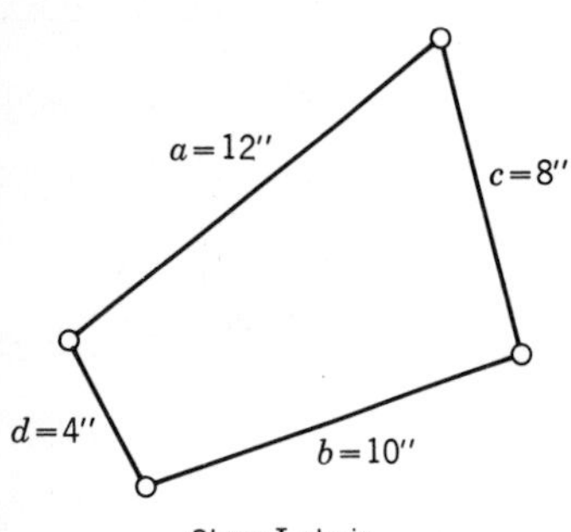

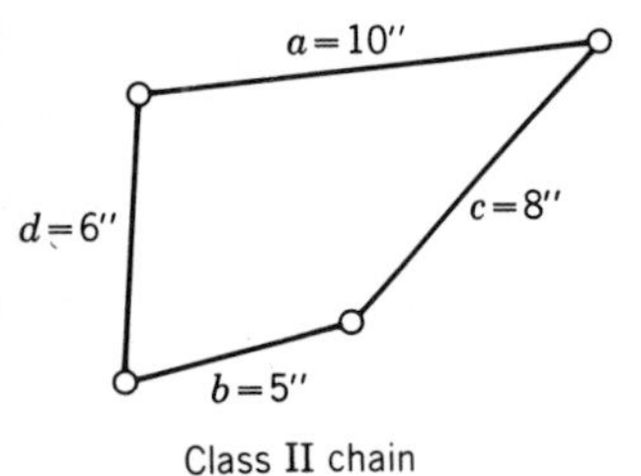

Fig. 3.2 Examples of class I and class II 4-bar chains.

3.2 *Mechanisms from class I chains*

Different mechanisms are formed by fixing different links of the chain. These different mechanisms are called "inversions" of the chain. Fig. 3.4 shows the inversions of a class I chain, with the limits of rotation of the cranks and levers indicated. With d fixed, a and b can rotate completely. With either a or b fixed, d can rotate completely and c oscillates. With c fixed, a and b can only oscillate (but d could be rotated if driven by a flexible shaft). These mechanisms have been given various names, among which are those shown in the figure.

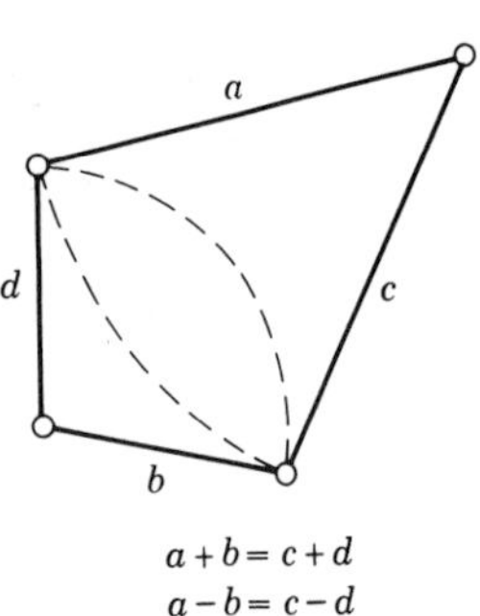

Fig. 3.3 The "isosceles" 4-bar, a borderline case in the classification.

3.3 *Mechanisms from class II chains*

Since, in this class, no link can execute a complete rotation relative to any other, all the mechanisms formed are "double-lever" mechanisms. A typical class II chain and the mechanisms formed from it are shown in Fig. 3.5.

3.4 *Two-position design: oscillating input and output*

A common problem is designing a mechanism to convert one oscillatory motion to another. The 4-bar mechanism (any class and any inversion) is the simplest and most logical way to do this in most cases.

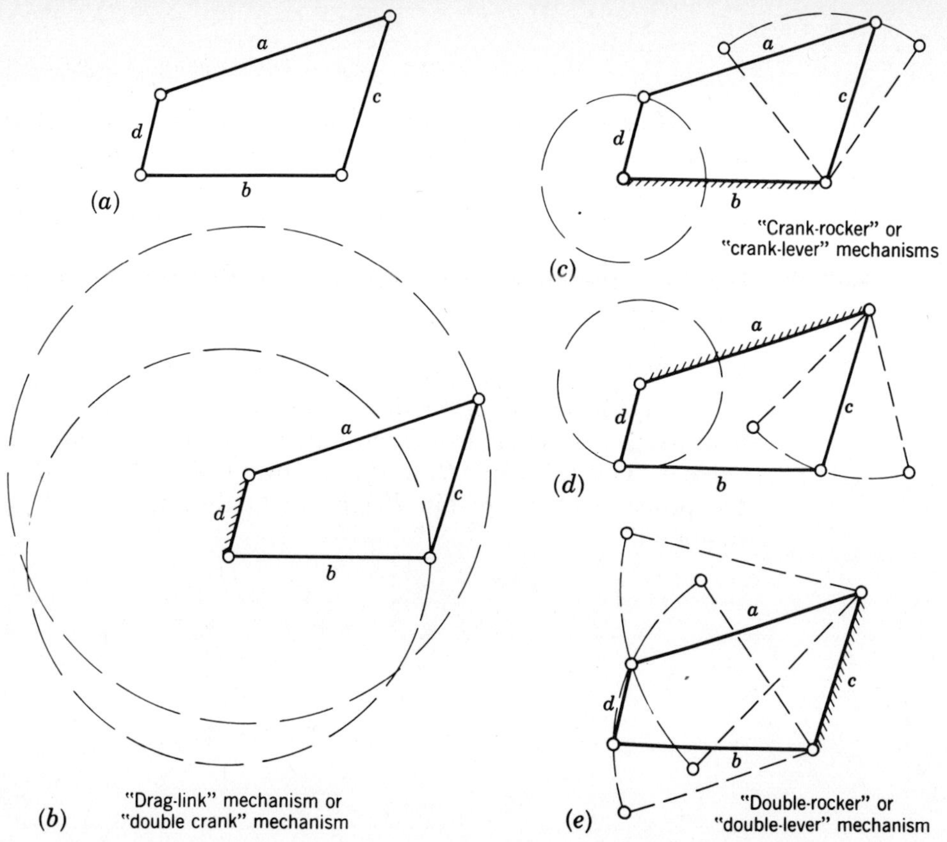

Fig. 3.4 Mechanisms formed by fixing different links of a class I 4-bar chain.

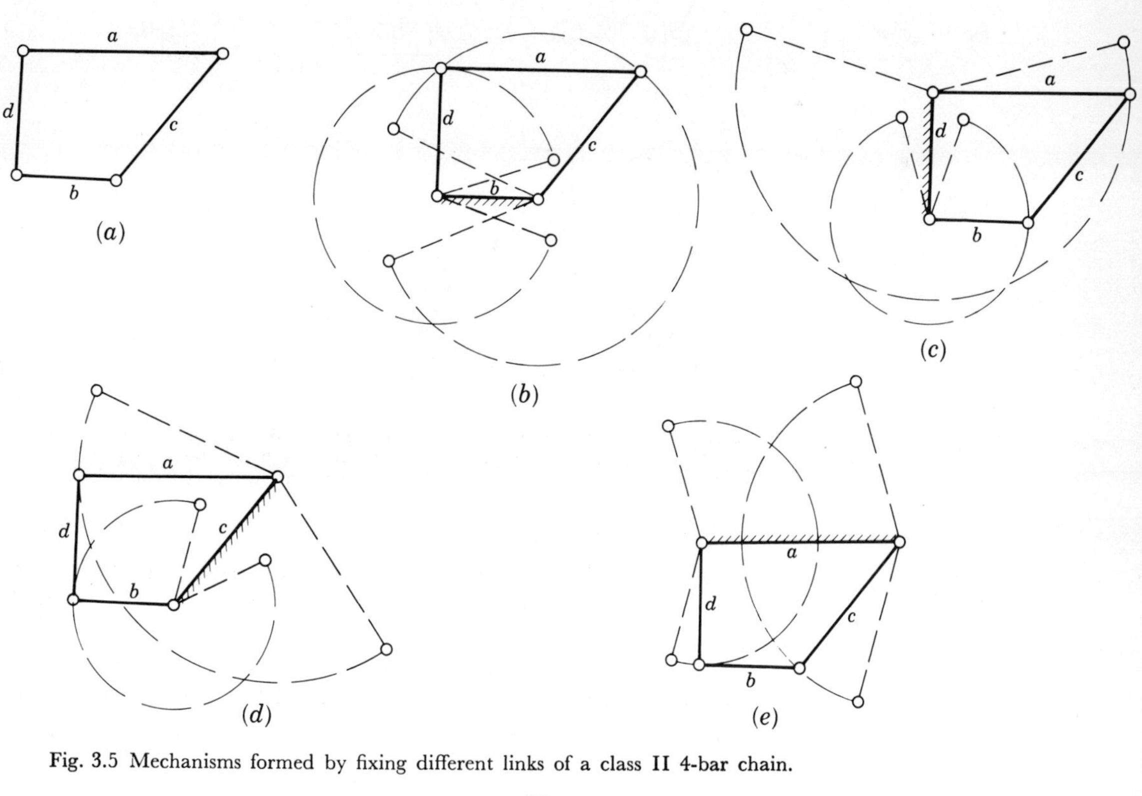

(a) (b) (c) (d) (e)

Fig. 3.5 Mechanisms formed by fixing different links of a class II 4-bar chain.

Consider the problem illustrated in Fig. 3.6(a). The input crank pivots at M and is to oscillate through angle θ between positions 1 and 2. At the same time the output crank, pivoted at Q, is to oscillate through angle ϕ between the limits indicated. The length of the output crank is specified, but the lengths of the input crank and the connecting rod are to be determined.

SOLUTION

(1) Invert the mechanism, visualizing the input crank held fixed in position 1 and the frame, MQ, rotated through angle θ. This will carry B_2 to B_2^1, as shown in Fig. 3.6(b). B_2^1 is the proper location of pin B relative to the input crank in position 2.

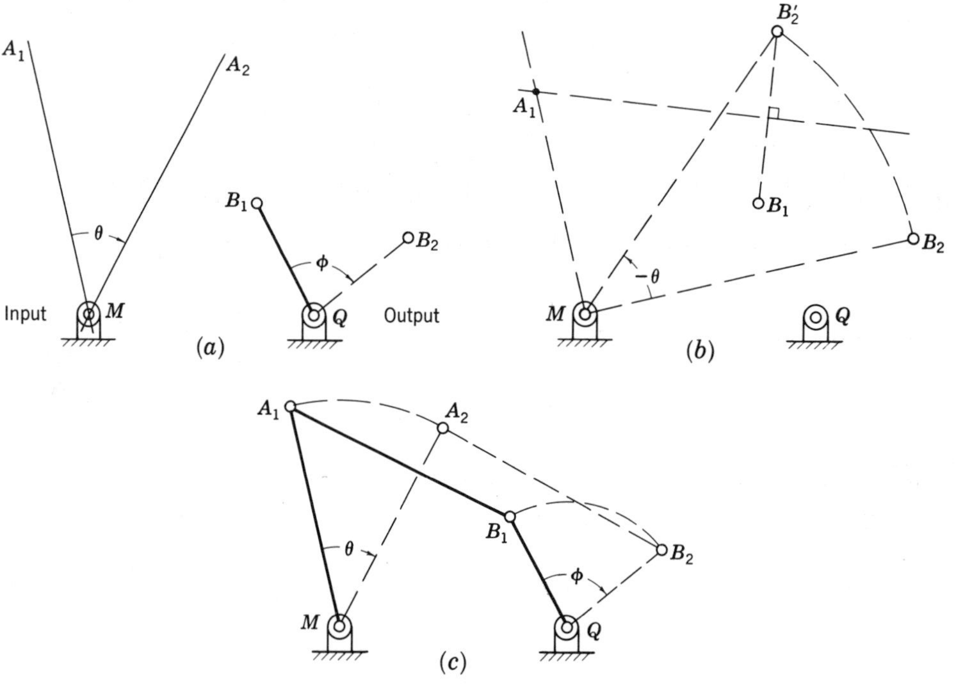

Fig. 3.6 A two-position design problem. The initial and final positions of the cranks and the length of one crank are specified. The lengths of the second crank and the connecting rod are to be determined.

(2) Pin A, where the connecting rod is joined to the input crank, must lie on the perpendicular bisector of $B_2^1B_1$. We draw this bisector and locate A_1 as shown in Fig. 3.6(b).

(3) The completed mechanism is as shown in Fig. 3.6(c). After the layout is completed, it should be checked by rotating the input crank through the specified angle θ and finding the angle through which the output crank moves.

While this is a rather elementary problem, it does illustrate some very useful ideas, particularly the use of inversion in the design process.

3.5 *The crank-lever mechanism*

In Fig. 3.7 a crank-lever mechanism is shown with the notation to be used in this discussion. As the crank (link 2) rotates, the lever (link 4) oscillates through angle θ. B_1 and B_2 are the two extreme positions of the pin at the end of the lever. A_1 and A_2 are the corresponding crankpin positions.

Notice that the two swings of the lever do not take place during equal crank rotation angles. The 4-bar functions as a "quick-return" mechanism. If the crank turns at constant speed, the time ratio of the two swings of the lever is

$$T.R. = \frac{180 + \alpha}{180 - \alpha}$$

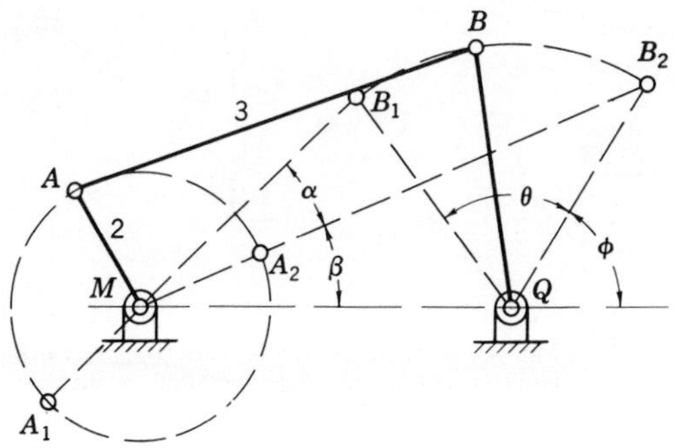

Fig. 3.7 Illustrating the notation used in discussing design of the crank-lever mechanism.

The most common design problem will be one in which the angle of oscillation, θ, and angle α (or the time ratio, which determines α) are specified. Specifying any two of the angles θ, α, β, ϕ determines a family of mechanisms from which the designer can choose a particular one on the basis of one of the other angles or some other criterion.

3.6 *Designing crank-lever mechanisms for specified θ and α: first method*

To design a crank-lever mechanism for a specified θ and α we can proceed as illustrated in Fig. 3.8.

(1) Start a layout by picking any point, Q, for the lever pivot and drawing an isosceles triangle QB_1B_2 with angle $B_1QB_2 = \theta$.

(2) Through B_2 draw a line B_2X. Through B_1 draw a line B_1Y at angle α with B_2X. The two lines intersect at M, a possible location for the crank pivot.

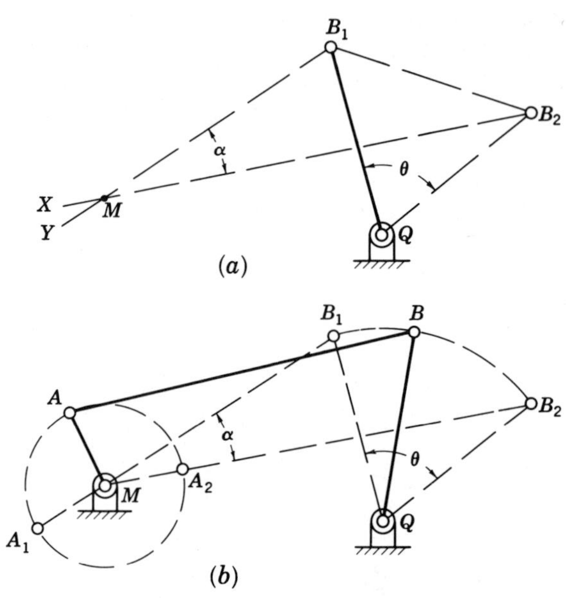

Fig. 3.8 One procedure for designing a crank-lever mechanism for specified θ and α.

(3) The lengths, L_2 of the crank and L_3 of the connecting rod, can now be determined from the following relations:

$$L_3 + L_2 = MB_2$$
$$L_3 - L_2 = MB_1$$

(4) The mechanism designed is shown in Fig. 3.8(b).

The above process is simple and leads quickly to a design. Since line B_2X was arbitrarily drawn, a great many different designs could be worked out. For positive α the locus of all possible locations for pivot M is the dark portion of the lower circle shown in Fig. 3.9. For a negative α the locus is the dark portion of the upper circle. The light portions of the circles are not possible locations for M because the lever would be required to swing past the line of pivots, MQ, an impossibility in the crank-lever mechanism.

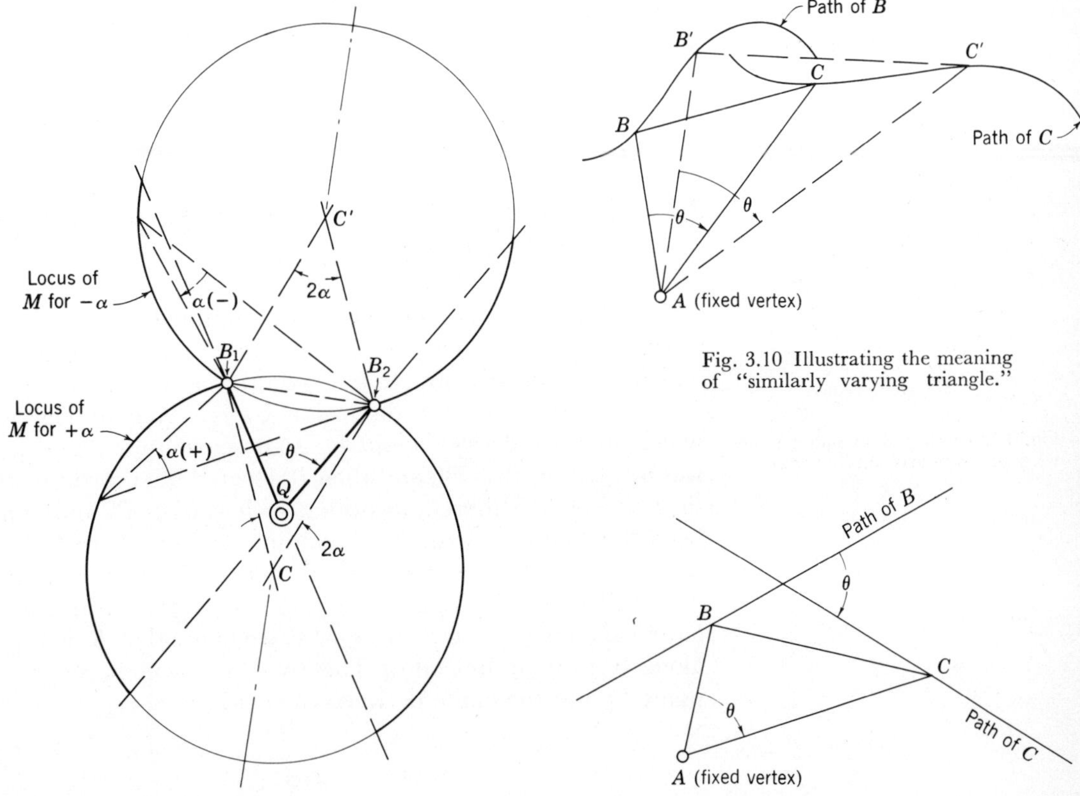

Fig. 3.9 Loci of possible locations for pivot M, for a specified θ and α.

Fig. 3.10 Illustrating the meaning of "similarly varying triangle."

Fig. 3.11 Straight-line loci for moving vertexes of a similarly varying triangle.

3.7 *Geometry: similarly varying triangles*

A triangle with one fixed vertex (the other two vertexes movable), varying in size and angular position but with all vertex angles remaining constant, is called a "similarly varying triangle." In linkage analysis and design it is frequently desirable to make use of such triangles.

As illustrated in Fig. 3.10, the two moving vertexes trace paths which are geometrically similar. The figure traced by C is larger than that traced by B in the ratio AC/AB and is rotated clockwise through the angle θ relative to the figure traced by B.

More particularly:

(1) If one moving vertex traces a straight line, so does the other. The two lines intersect at angle θ, the angle at the fixed vertex of the similarly varying triangle. See Fig. 3.11.

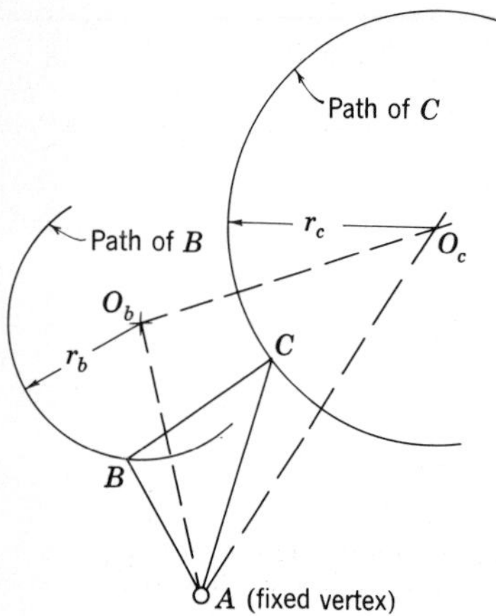

Fig. 3.12 Circle loci for moving vertexes of a similarly varying triangle.

(2) If one moving vertex traces a circle, so does the other. The ratio of the radii of the two circles is $r_c/r_b = AC/AB$. Furthermore, the triangle AO_cO_b is similar to the varying triangle ACB. See Fig. 3.12.

We shall make use of these facts in the next article.

3.8 *Designing crank-lever mechanisms for specified θ and β: second method*

While the design procedure outlined in Art. 3.6 is straightforward and easy to explain, there is another procedure which has some advantages but requires more explanation.

(1) We start the discussion by referring to Fig. 3.13, which shows a design layout for some particular θ and β. B_2 was located arbitrarily, and then B_1 located in accordance with the value of θ. Different locations, such as B_2' or B_2'', might have been chosen for B_2, with corresponding locations B_1' or B_1'' for B_1. See Fig. 3.14. We see that we have here a picture of a similarly varying triangle, QB_1B_2, with Q the fixed vertex. Since we are letting B_2 move along the line MX, we know that B_1 will move along a straight line also. The two lines will intersect at a point B_1^0 and the angle between them will be θ.

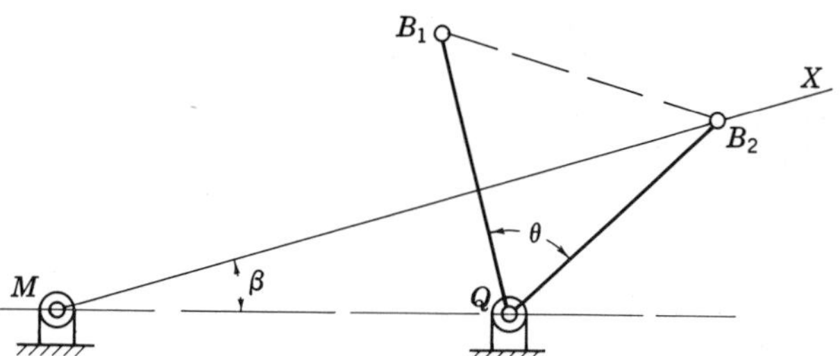

Fig. 3.13 Design layout for a particular θ and β.

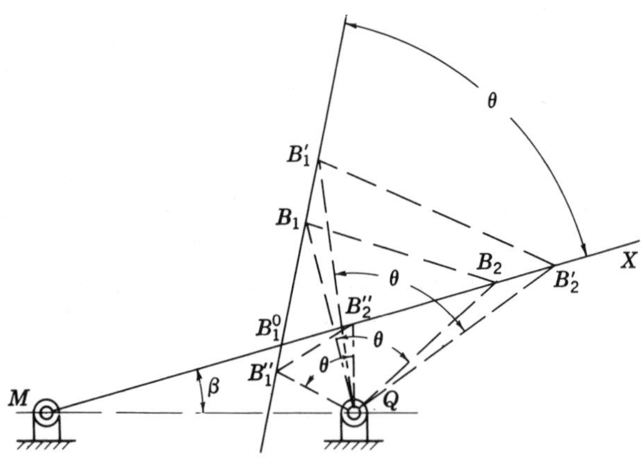

Fig. 3.14 Effect of choosing different locations for B_2.

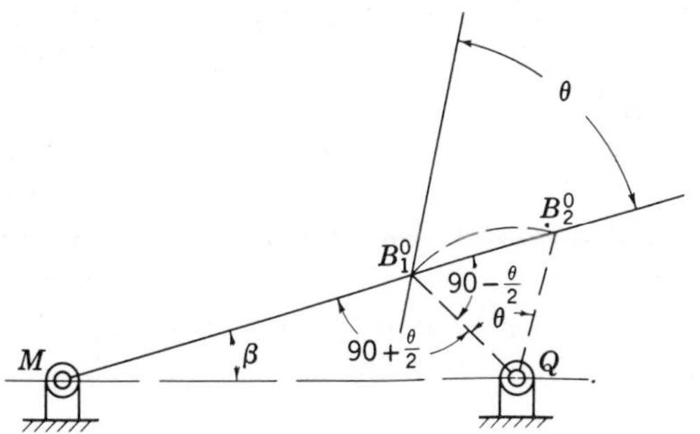

Fig. 3.15 Some angle relations.

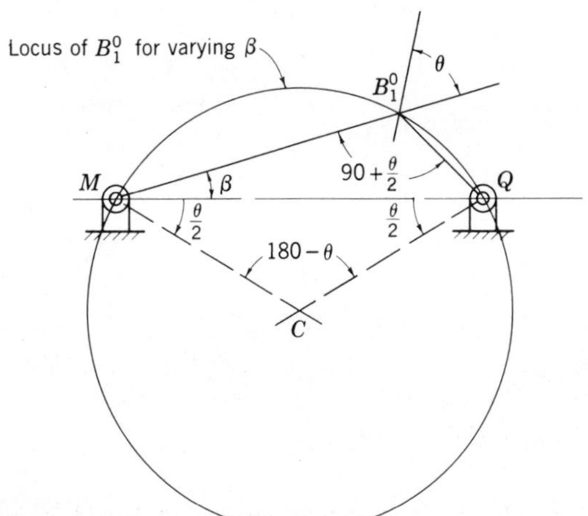

Fig. 3.16 Locus of B_1^0 obtained by varying β while θ is held constant.

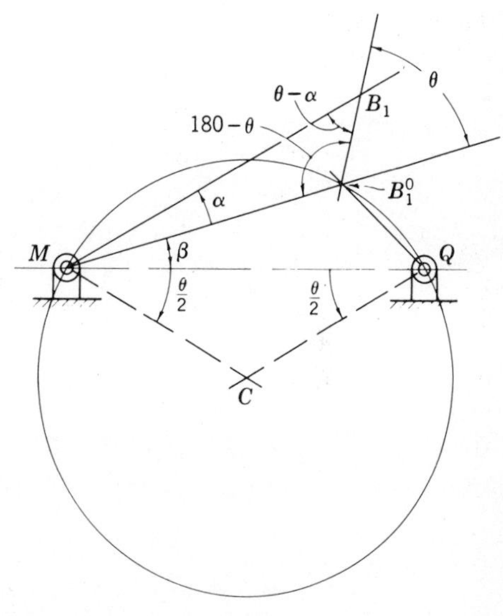

Fig. 3.17 Some further angle relationships. For a constant α and θ, but varying β, triangle $MB_1^0B_1$ is a similarly varying triangle.

(2) We next refer to Fig. 3.15 to establish the fact that angle MB_1^0Q is equal to $90 + (\theta/2)$. We do this by noting that, if B_1 were chosen at B_1^0, B_2 would be located at B_2^0 and angle $QB_1^0B_2^0$ is $90 - (\theta/2)$.

The important conclusion here is that *angle MB_1^0Q is independent of β*. For a different choice of β this angle would still be $90 + (\theta/2)$.

(3) We now consider the locus of B_1^0 for varying β. We have established that point B_1^0 sees the MQ line under angle $90 + (\theta/2)$. Hence the locus of B_1^0 for varying β (but constant θ) is the circle shown in Fig. 3.16.

(4) We have not yet brought angle α into the discussion. In Fig. 3.17 we choose a value for α and thus determine a location for B_1. We next examine the angles in the triangle $MB_1^0B_1$. Angle $MB_1^0B_1 = 180 - \theta$. Hence angle $MB_1B_1^0$ is

$$180 - [(180 - \theta) + \alpha]$$

or

$$(\theta - \alpha)$$

The important conclusion here is that *the angles in triangle* $MB_1^0B_1$ *are independent of* β. *For varying* β *triangle* $MB_1^0B_1$ *is a similarly varying triangle.*

(5) We have previously established that, for varying β, the locus of B_1^0 is the circle with center C, shown in Fig. 3.16 and again in Fig. 3.18. Since B_1 is the second moving vertex of similarly varying triangle $MB_1^0B_1$, its locus is also a circle. The center, G, for this circle must be so located that triangle MCG is similar to triangle $MB_1^0B_1$. This is shown in Fig. 3.18.

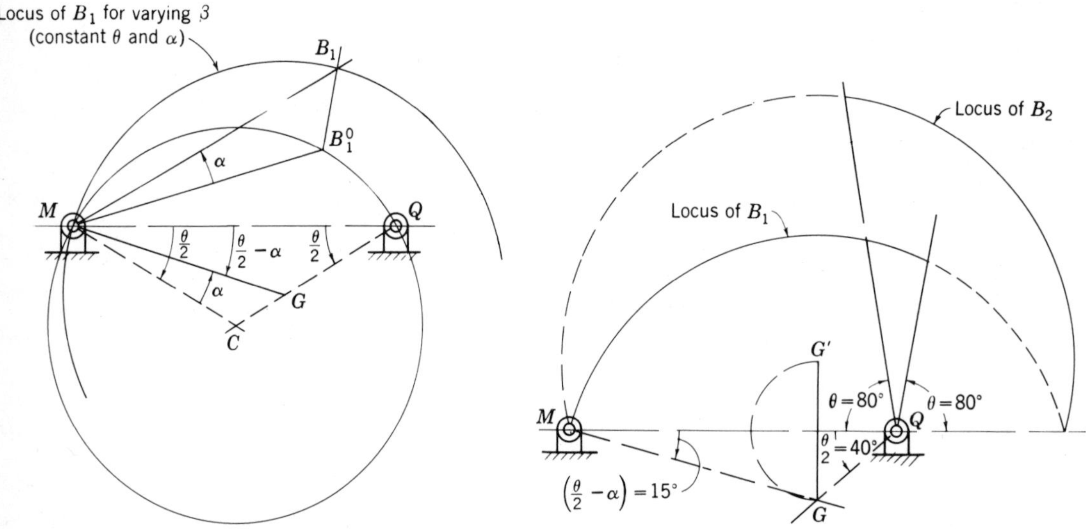

Fig. 3.18 For constant α and θ, but varying β, locus of B_1 is the circle with center G.

Fig. 3.19 Layout for determining loci of B_1 and B_2 in the design problem for which $\theta = 40$ deg. and $\alpha = 25$ deg.

This rather lengthy discussion has led up to a very simple design procedure, which we now outline, using an example with numerical values. We shall design for $\theta = 80$ deg. and $\alpha = 25$ deg.

(1) Start a layout by choosing a pivot distance MQ. See Fig. 3.19.

(2) Draw line MG at angle $\theta/2 - \alpha$ (clockwise if positive) with line MQ. In our example $\theta/2 - \alpha = +15$ deg.

(3) Draw line QG at angle $\theta/2 = 40$ deg. (counterclockwise) with line QM. Point G, the center of the circle locus for B_1, has now been located. The locus for B_2 is the circle with center G' and radius $G'M$, where G' and G are symmetrically located with respect to line MQ. This is easily proved by noting that QB_1B_2 is a similarly varying triangle. The usable portions of the loci are shown by heavy lines. Locating B_1 or B_2 outside these limits would require the impossible action of swinging the lever past the MQ line.

(4) Particular designs can now be picked off the layout and compared. Two sample designs are shown in Fig. 3.20.

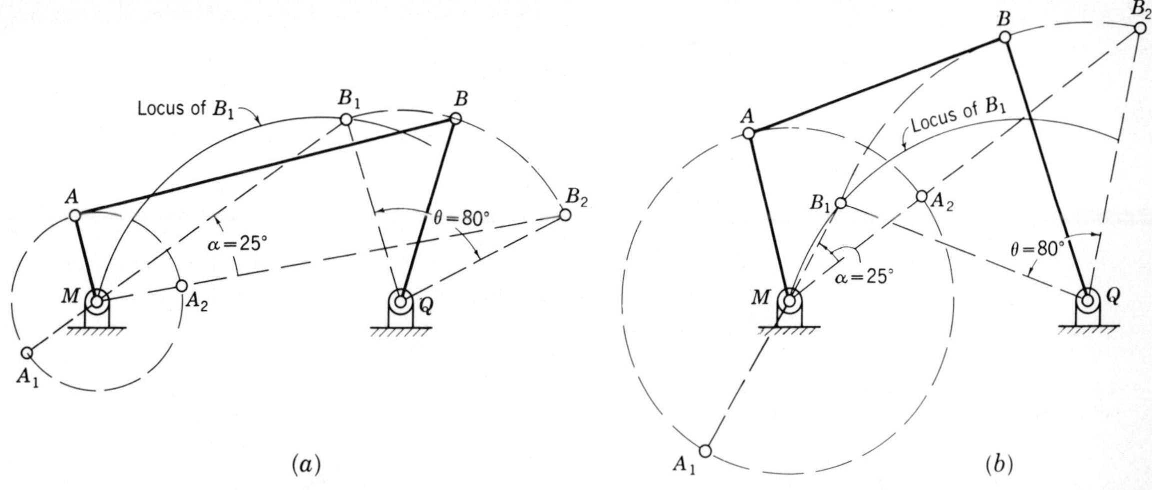

Fig. 3.20 Sample designs picked from the layout of Fig. 3.19.

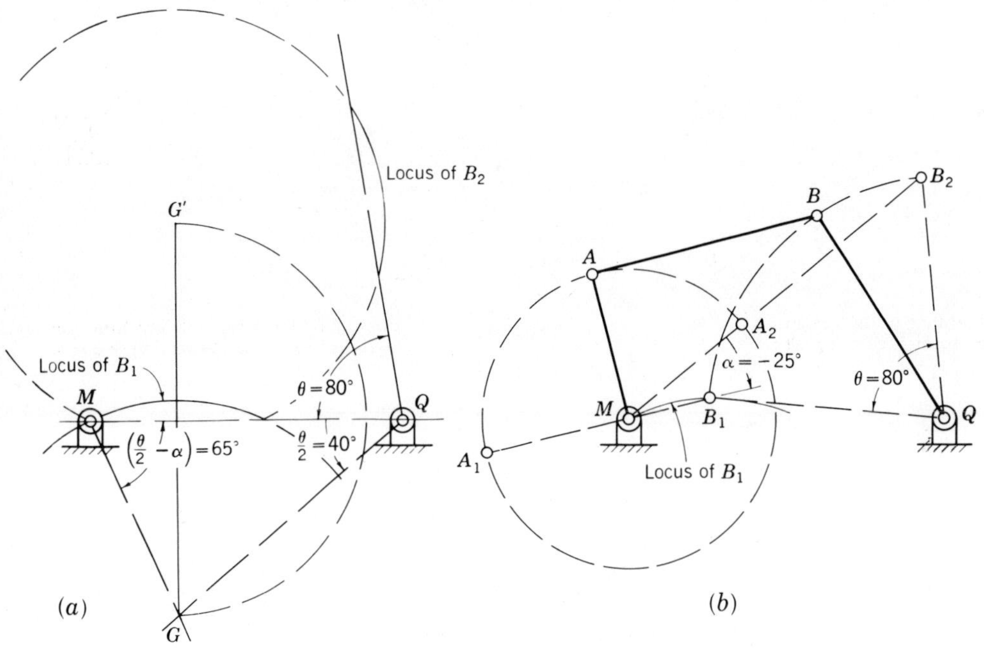

Fig. 3.21 Layout and one sample design for $\theta = 40$ deg. and $\alpha = -25$ deg.

Final decision would depend on the requirements of the particular application. For example, if it is necessary to keep maximum angular acceleration of the oscillating lever as low as possible, the tentative designs should be analyzed for this property.

The preceding example and discussion were for a positive angle α. The same discussion applies for negative α. For comparison with Figs. 3.19 and 3.20, we show in Fig. 3.21 the layout and one sample design for $\theta = 80$ deg. and $\alpha = -25$ deg.

3.9 *Special case:* $\alpha = \theta$

This special situation gives rise to a family of mechanisms which includes the familiar crank-shaper inversion of the slider-crank mechanism. As shown in Fig. 3.22, the two lines *MG* and *QG* are parallel. The center, *G*, of the circle locus for B_1 is at infinity, and the locus is the straight line indicated. B_1 may be chosen anywhere on this line. One design is shown in Fig. 3.23.

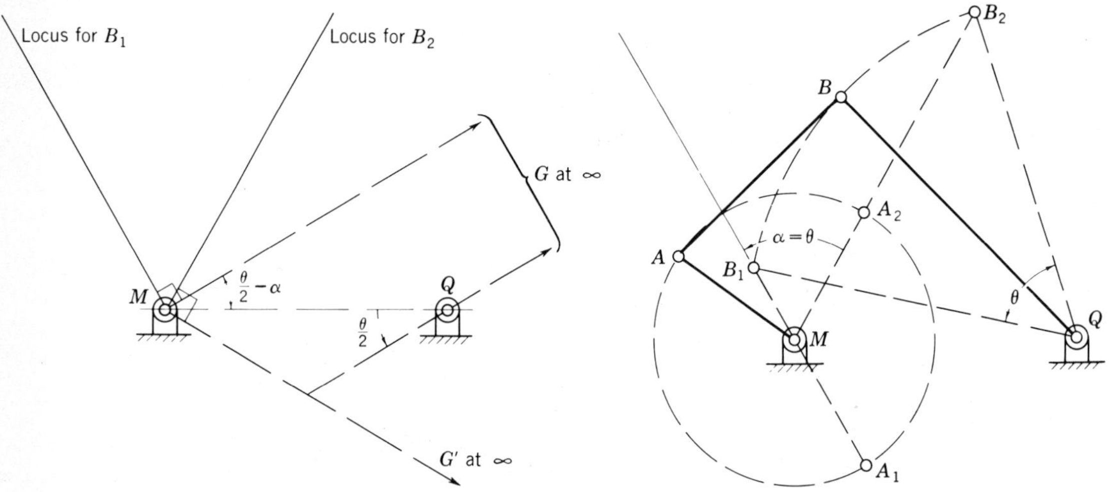

Fig. 3.22 Appearance of the design layout for the special case $\alpha = \theta$.

Fig. 3.23 One sample design from the layout of Fig. 3.22. Special case $\alpha = \theta$.

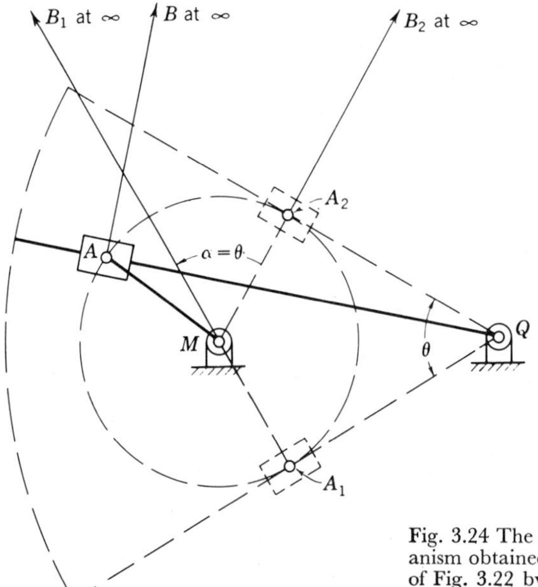

Fig. 3.24 The crank-shaper mechanism obtained from design layout of Fig. 3.22 by choosing B_1 to be a point at infinity on the B_1 locus.

Among the possible choices for B_1 is the point at infinity. This requires an infinitely long connecting rod and oscillating lever, which is accomplished mechanically by use of straight slider joints. The resulting mechanism, shown in Fig. 3.24, will be recognized as the crank-shaper inversion of the slider-crank mechanism.

3.10 *Transmission angle*

The angle between the connecting rod and the output lever or crank of a 4-bar mechanism, called the "transmission angle," is illustrated in Fig. 3.25. From the force-transmission standpoint, especially in the presence of appreciable joint friction, it is desirable to have this angle deviate from 90 deg. as little as possible within the range of motion over which the mechanism is to operate. In other words, $|90 - \mu|_{max}$ is considered one "figure of merit" in comparing alternate possible designs for a particular application.

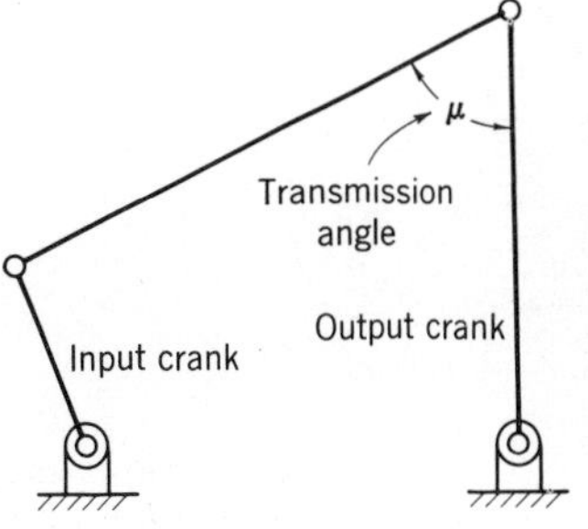

Fig. 3.25 Definition of "transmission angle."

For the crank-lever mechanism, operated through a full revolution of the driving crank, extreme values of μ are reached when the crank is in line with the pivots, as illustrated in Fig. 3.26. For this case $|90 - \mu|_{max}$ would be either $|90 - \mu_{max}|$ or $|90 - \mu_{min}|$, whichever was the larger.

In addition to force transmission there is another reason for concern over the transmission angle, particularly in the "computing linkage" type of application, where close coordination of the crank motions is desired. A "poor" transmission angle—large $|90 - \mu|$—makes the position of the output crank more sensitive to clearances in the joints, manufacturing tolerances on link lengths, and changes in dimension due to thermal expansions. No rigid value can be stated for acceptable limits to the value of $|90 - \mu|_{max}$, but some designers suggest 45 deg. as a maximum desirable value for general practice.

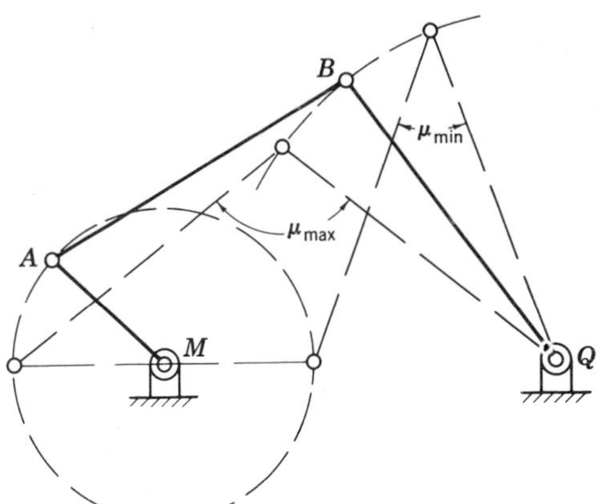

Fig. 3.26 Showing maximum and minimum values of transmission angle, μ, in the crank-lever mechanism.

3.11 *Designing for optimum transmission angle*

To find the optimum design from the transmission-angle standpoint when α and θ are specified, make the basic layout for the crank-lever mechanism and pick off a series of designs. For each design find $|90 - \mu|_{max}$ and interpolate to find the mechanism for which this is minimum. The interpolation need not be highly precise because usually designs somewhere near the theoretical optimum are equally good for all practical purposes.

Fig. 3.27 shows the layout, graphical interpolation, and mechanism finally selected for $\theta = 90$ deg., $\alpha = 20$ deg. Optimum value of $|90 - \mu|_{max}$ turns out to be approximately 61.5 deg. for this case.

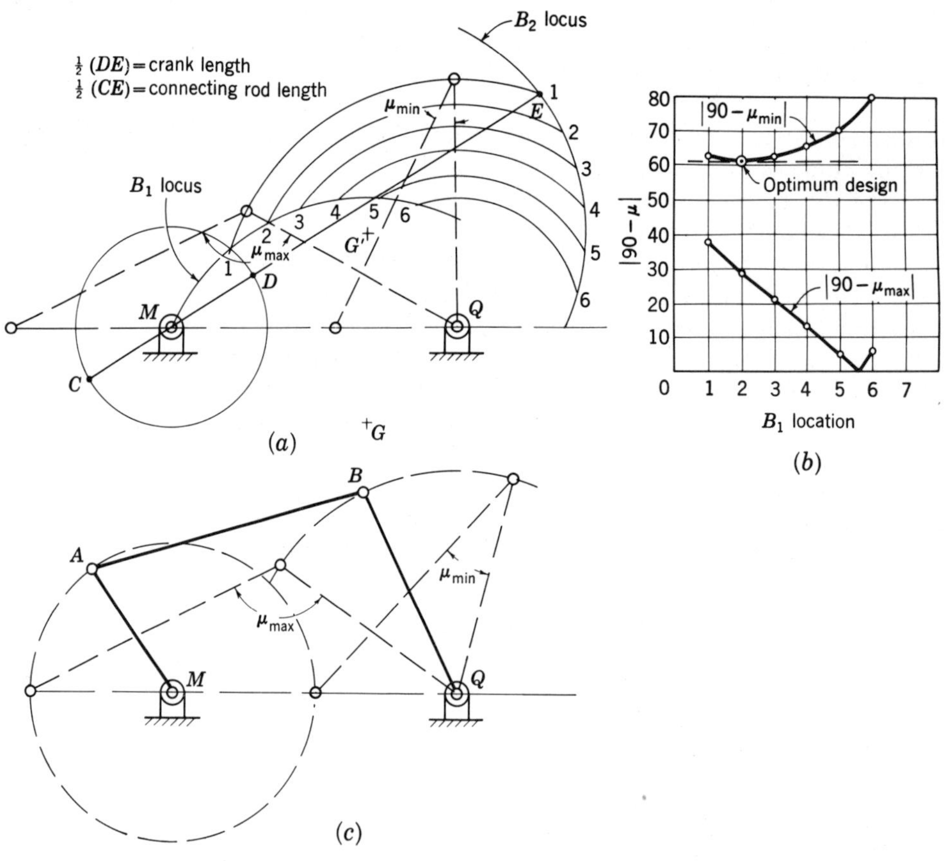

Fig. 3.27 Illustrating a procedure for finding the design with optimum transmission angle.

3.12 *Linkage-gear combinations for large output oscillation angles*

Output oscillation angles greater than 180 deg. cannot be produced by the crank-lever 4-bar alone. Practically, the limit is much less than 180 deg. because of the poor transmission angles encountered. Two ways of combining gearing with the 4-bar to produce large output angles are illustrated in Fig. 3.28.

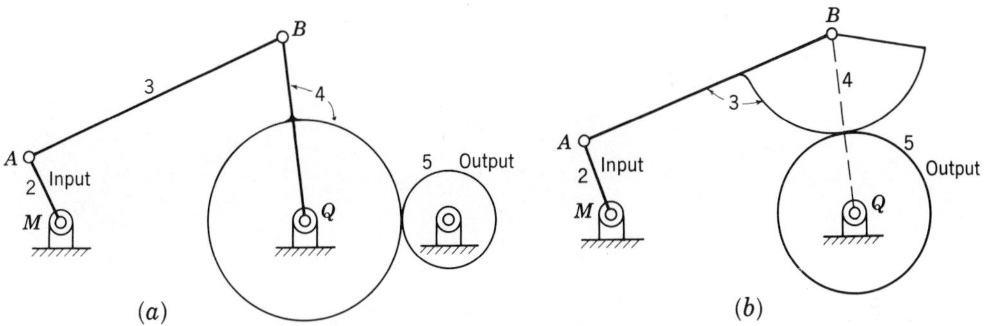

Fig. 3.28 Linkage-gear combinations for large output oscillation angles.

The first scheme [Fig. 3.28(a)] involves a gear compounded with the output lever of the 4-bar and driving a smaller gear which is the final output link of the mechanism. The design problem here is quite simple. For example, if an output oscillation of 180 deg. is desired, we might design the 4-bar for a 90 deg. oscillation of the lever and then use a 2 to 1 ratio of gearing.

The second scheme [Fig. 3.28(b)] involves a gear, made a part of link 3 (the connecting rod) and centered at pin B, in mesh with another gear (link 5) coaxial with the lever. In this way the motion of 3 relative to 4, as modified by the gear ratio, is added to the motion of 4 to produce the total motion of output gear 5. Total oscillation angle, to a first rough approximation, will be $\theta + n(\mu_{max} - \mu_{min})$, where n is the gear ratio. Since the extremes of μ are not reached at the same crank positions as the extremes of the oscillating lever, the total oscillation angle will be somewhat less than the above value. The following is suggested as a possible design procedure.

(1) Select a gear ratio, n. This should be, very approximately, $n = \gamma/\theta - 1$, where γ is the oscillation angle desired for the output gear and θ is the lever oscillation angle for which the

4-bar will be designed. A practical upper limit for θ is around 100 deg. For an illustration we shall design for $\gamma = 180$ deg., use $n = 1$, and make θ approximately 90 deg.

(2) Design the 4-bar for $a = 0$ and the approximate value of θ chosen. For our example, if θ is to be made 90 deg., $\mu_{max} - \mu_{min}$ must be slightly larger than 90 deg. A preliminary layout shows that $\mu_{max} - \mu_{min}$ will be considerably more than 90 deg. for all practical 4-bars of the $a = 0$, $\theta = 90$ family. Hence it was decided to try $\theta = 88$ deg., for which the layout is shown in Fig. 3.29.

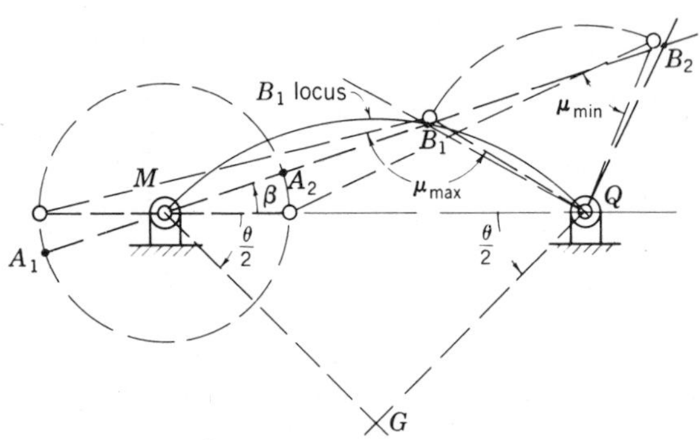

Fig. 3.29 Layout for linkage-gear design problem.

(3) The difference in crank rotation angle at which extremes of μ and of lever oscillation occur is angle β. If we were to plot lever angular displacement and μ versus crank position, we should obtain two curves, resembling sine curves, out of phase by angle β. Two sine curves, of amplitudes $n\mu_a$ and θ_a, out of phase by angle β, when added result in a sine curve of amplitude

$$\gamma_a = \sqrt{(\theta_a + n\mu_a)^2 - 2n\theta_a\mu_a(1 - \cos\beta)}$$

Hence, if for a tentative design we simply find μ_{max} and μ_{min}, and thus

$$n\mu_a = 1/2\, n\,(\mu_{max} - \mu_{min})$$

we can quickly estimate the amplitude, γ_a, of the output oscillation.

For our numerical problem $\theta_a = \theta/2 = 44$ deg. After a few trials a 4-bar was found for which $\beta = 18$ deg., $\mu_{max} = 137.0$ deg., and $\mu_{min} = 43.2$ deg.

$$n\mu_a = 1/2(1)\,(137.0 - 43.2) = 46.9$$

$$\gamma_a = \sqrt{(44 + 46.9)^2 - 2(44)\,(46.9)\,(1 - \cos 18)} = 89.8 \text{ deg.}$$

Estimate of output oscillation angle is then 2(89.8) = 179.6 deg.

(4) The designed mechanism is shown in Fig. 3.30. Our graphical layout and design calculations are good to no better than ±0.5 deg. Further checking and refinement of the design would have to be done by computation.

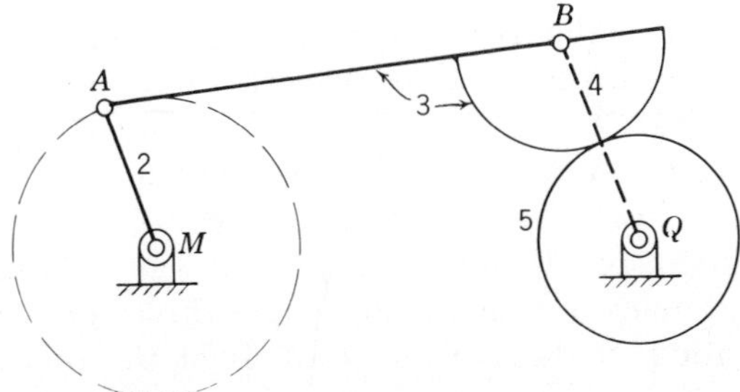

Fig. 3.30 Mechanism designed from layout of Fig. 3.29 and calculations of Art. 3.12.

3.13 *Overlay for coordinated crank motions*

The design problems discussed so far have been essentially of the "two-position" type. No control has been exercised over the details of motion intermediate between the two design positions. Later chapters will consider theoretically exact means for dealing with more than two positions, but we include here one very practical approximate way of designing for multiply-coordinated input- and output-crank positions. The procedure, which is called the "overlay method," will be illustrated by the following example.

PROBLEM STATEMENT

A 4-bar mechanism is to be designed so that the angular displacements of the two cranks will be related according to the following schedule:

Position Number	Degrees rotation from starting position: First Crank	Degrees rotation from starting position: Second Crank
0	0	0
1	30	17
2	60	36
3	90	59
4	120	88

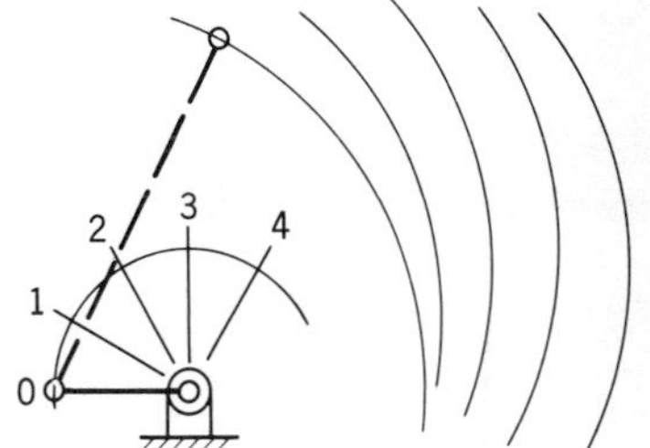

Fig. 3.31 The overlay method. Layout showing successive positions of the first crank, an assumed connecting-rod length, and loci of positions of the extreme end of the rod.

PROCEDURE

(1) On tracing paper make a layout (Fig. 3.31) showing the successive positions of the first crank. Use any convenient

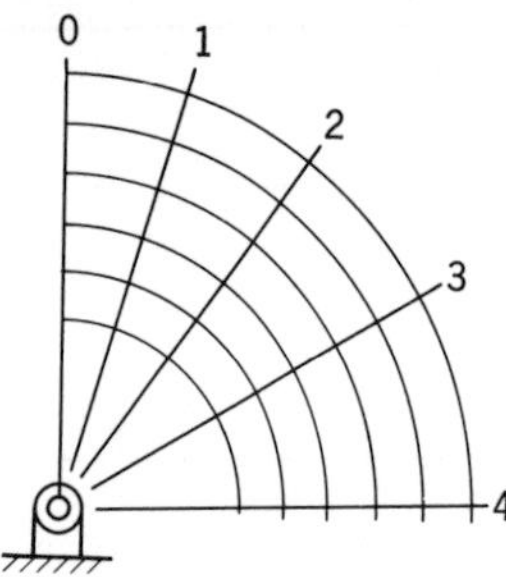

Fig. 3.32 The overlay method. Required positions of the second crank corresponding to positions of the first crank shown in Fig. 3.31.

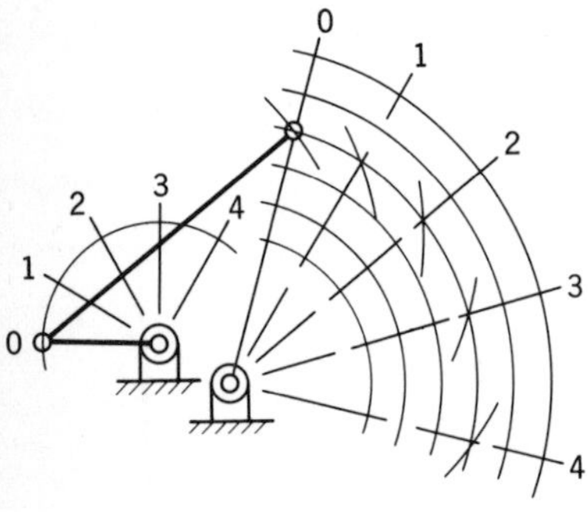

Fig. 3.33 Overlay of layouts in Figs. 3.31 and 3.32, fitted to determine unknown dimensions of the 4-bar mechanism.

length for this crank. Assume a length for the connecting rod, and draw the family of circle arcs of this radius with centers at the successive crankpin positions.

(2) Make a second layout (Fig. 3.32) showing the successive positions of the second crank and a series of possible lengths for this crank.

(3) Fit the first layout over the second, as shown in Fig. 3.33, trying to make the circle arcs of the first pass, in proper order, through one of the series of possible crankpin positions of the second. It may be necessary to try other connecting-rod lengths, redrawing the first layout, before a satisfactory fit is obtained or the conclusion is drawn that none exists.

This is a good, practical procedure that will yield satisfactory results for many problems, especially those for which tolerance on position of the output crank is of the order of 0.5 deg. or more.

Problems and Exercises

E3.1 Refer to Fig. 3.34. Complete the design of the 4-bar mechanism so that, as the crank pivoted at *Q* turns clockwise through the 90-deg. angle indicated, the crank pivoted at *M* will turn counterclockwise through the 60-deg. angle indicated.

E3.2 Design a crank-lever mechanism such that, with the crank turning at constant speed, the oscillating lever will have a time ratio of advance to return of 3 to 2. The lever is to oscillate through an angle of 80 deg. Find a design which is close to optimum from the transmission-angle standpoint.

E3.3 Design a linkage-gear mechanism of the type shown in Fig. 3.28(b). The output oscillation angle is to be 200 ± 1 deg. Use a gear ratio, n, of 3 to 1.

E3.4 A 4-bar mechanism is to be designed so that the motions of the two cranks will be coordinated according to the following schedule.

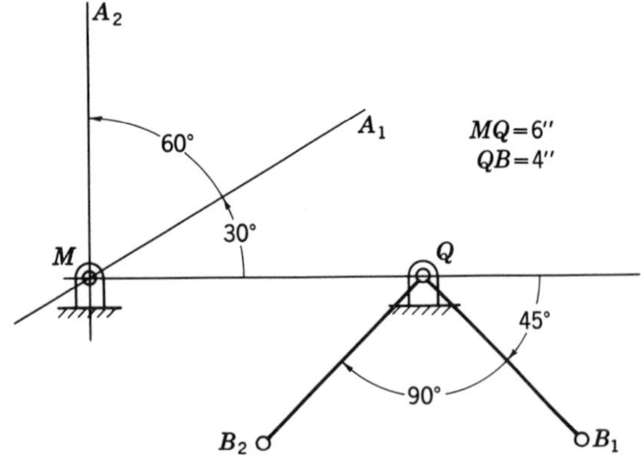

Fig. 3.34 Partial layout for problem E3.1.

Position Number	Degrees rotation from starting position: First Crank (clockwise)	Second Crank (counterclockwise)
0	0	0.0
1	15	15.8
2	30	33.0
3	45	52.4
4	60	73.3
5	75	96.3

(Note: This is the function $\phi = -\theta e^{\theta/300}$, $0 < \theta < 75$, computed with slide-rule accuracy. $\theta =$ first crank rotation angle and $\phi =$ second crank rotation angle.)

Use the overlay method discussed in Art. 3.13.

E3.5 Design a spring-linkage counterbalancing system of the type shown in Fig. 3.35. The weight, W, is 50 lb and the pulley radius is 12 in. It is required that the weight be counterbalanced over a 90-deg. range of pulley rotation, i.e., within this range the weight should remain in any position in which it is placed. Neglecting friction, this would mean that the force exerted by link 3 on crank 4 should have a moment about the pivot just equal to the moment WR. However, it is anticipated that there will be enough friction in the joints so that it will be necessary to balance the moment WR only within $\pm 3\%$.

The spring is to be assumed linear and is to be assembled so that the spring torque (exerted on crank 2) will range from T_i to $2T_i$ over the counterbalancing range. Design for a 90-deg. range of motion for crank 2.

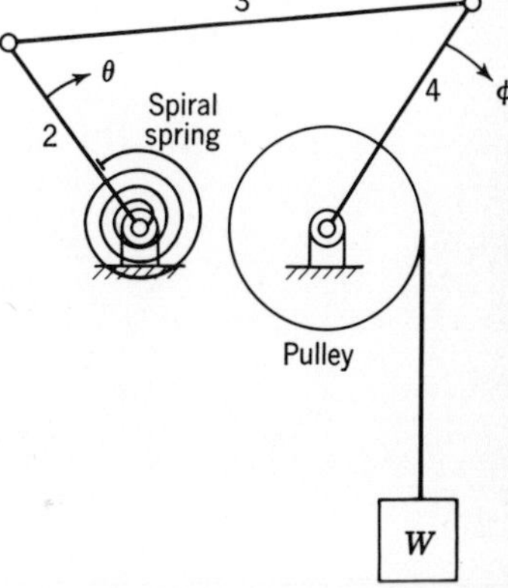

Fig. 3.35 General scheme of spring-linkage counterbalance to be designed in problem E3.5.

(a) What initial spring torque, T_i, is required?

(b) What is the necessary functional relation between the rotation angle, ϕ, of crank 4 and the rotation angle, θ, of crank 2? (Measure ϕ and θ from the "initial" position, i.e., the position when the weight is at the upper end of its range.) For a series of values of θ calculate the required ϕ.

(c) Use the overlay method to find a tentative design for the 4-bar linkage. You may choose to design so that the two cranks turn either in the same or in opposite directions.

(d) When you have a tentative design, check to find whether it accomplishes the desired purpose within the 3% limits. Analyze carefully to see how best to make this check. (Hint: You will probably find it useful to determine the angular velocity ratio of the two cranks for a series of positions throughout the range of motion.)

4

Coupler curves

4.1 *Definition and equation*

The paths traced by points belonging to the connecting rod, or "coupler," of a 4-bar mechanism are called "coupler curves." Samples are shown in Fig. 4.1. These curves are of sixth order and, as shown, can have rather complicated shapes, with as many as three "double points." Beyer (3) gives the following as one form of the equation for the coupler curve:

$$a^2[(x-k)^2+y^2](x^2+y^2+b^2-r^2)^2-2ab[(x^2+y^2-kx)\cos\gamma+ky\sin\gamma](x^2+y^2+b^2-r^2)[(x-k)^2+y^2+a^2-R^2]+b^2(x^2+y^2)[(x-k)^2+y^2+a^2-R^2]^2-4a^2b^2[(x^2+y^2-kx)\sin\gamma-ky\cos\gamma]^2=0$$

Notation is as shown in Fig. 4.2.

4.2 *Roberts' law*

In the linkage of Fig. 4.3 the triangles *GFC, CED, ACB, MOQ, GOD, AEQ*, and *MFB* are similar. It is a property of this linkage that all these triangles remain similar when the links are displaced relative to each other. In Fig. 4.4 the same linkage has been redrawn with the links displaced from their relative positions in Fig. 4.3 and with pins *O, Q*, and *M* made fixed

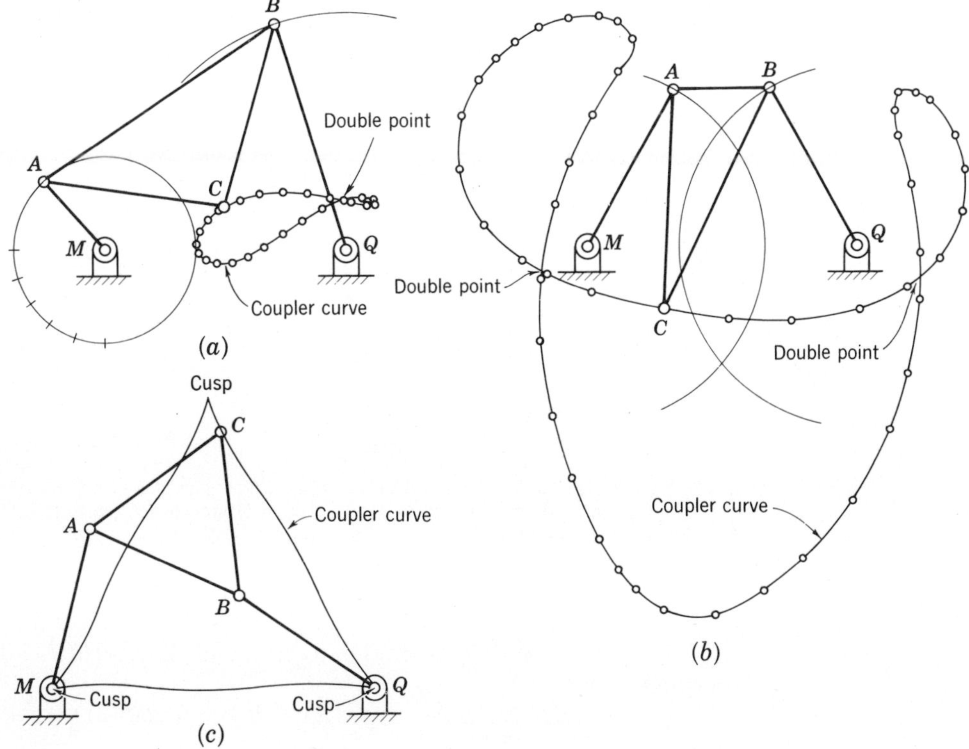

Fig. 4.1 Some sample coupler curves.

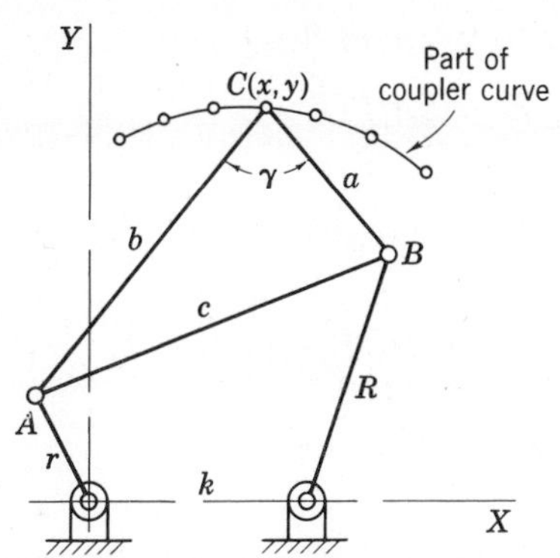

Fig. 4.2 Notation used in the coupler-curve equation of Art. 4.1.

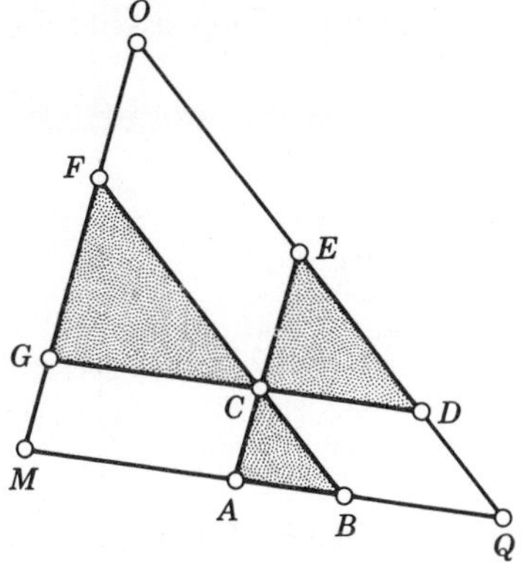

Fig. 4.3 Roberts' linkage.

pivots. This creates three different 4-bar mechanism with their couplers pinned together at *C*. If it can be proved that this combination of 4-bars is movable, it will be established that three different 4-bar mechanisms trace the same coupler curve (path of *C*). Consider Fig. 4.5, in which a portion of the mechanism has been redrawn from Fig. 4.4.

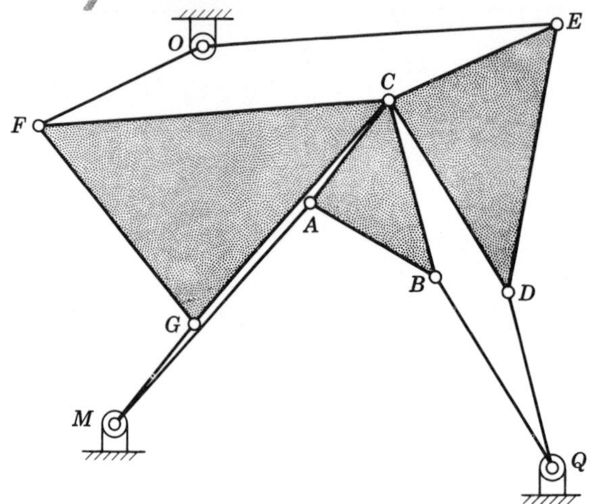

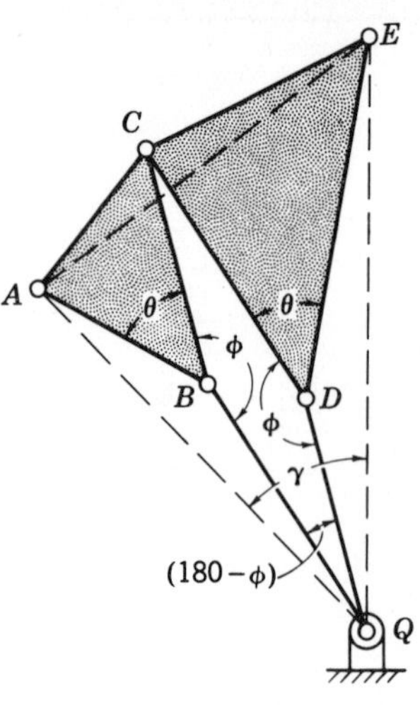

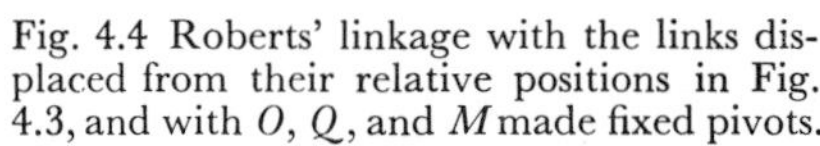

Fig. 4.4 Roberts' linkage with the links displaced from their relative positions in Fig. 4.3, and with O, Q, and M made fixed pivots.

Fig. 4.5 A part of Fig. 4.4 redrawn. Used to prove that QAE is a similarly varying triangle.

(1) Triangle ACB is similar to triangle CED. $QBCD$ is a parallelogram.

(2) $CD/DE = AB/BC$, but $CD = BQ$ and $BC = QD$, so

$$BQ/DE = AB/DQ$$

Also angle

$$QBA = \text{angle } EDQ = 360 - (\theta + \phi)$$

Triangle QDE is therefore similar to triangle ABQ. So

$$QA/QE = BA/QD = BA/BC$$

(3) Angle $\gamma = \text{angle } AQB + \text{angle } DQE + (180 - \phi)$. But angle AQB = angle QED (similar triangles proved above). Hence

$$\begin{aligned} \text{angle } \gamma &= \text{angle } QED + \text{angle } DQE + (180 - \phi) \\ &= 180 - \text{angle } EDQ + (180 - \phi) \\ &= -180 + (\theta + \phi) + (180 - \phi) \\ &= \theta \end{aligned}$$

(4) Since $QA/QE = BA/BC$, and $\gamma = \theta$ (proved above), triangle QAE is similar to triangles BAC and DCE. Triangle QAE is therefore a similarly varying triangle.

(5) In a similarly varying triangle, if one free vertex is guided to move on a circle, the other free vertex will also move on a circle. Furthermore, the centers of these two circles plus the fixed vertex of the varying triangle are the vertexes of a triangle similar to the varying triangle.

If point E is guided to move on a circle by means of a crank pivoted at O (Fig. 4.4), point A will move on a circle with center M, such that triangle QMO is similar to triangle QAE.

A crank may be pinned at *A* and pivoted at *M* without locking the mechanism. Thus the two 4-bar mechanisms *OEDQ* and *MABQ* in Fig. 4.4 are movable, even though their couplers are pinned together at *C*. Hence these two 4-bars must cause *C* to trace identical coupler curves.

(6) An argument similar to the above would show that triangle *MFB* is also a similarly varying triangle and hence that the 4-bars *OFGM* and *MABQ* must cause *C* to trace identical coupler curves.

The proposition that any coupler curve is traced by three different 4-bar mechanisms was first proved by S. Roberts in 1875. It has uses in both analysis and design as will be shown by examples later.

4.3 *Coupler curves from 5-bar mechanisms*

In 1878, Chebychev, in Russia, independently arrived at Roberts' law. Probably Chebychev is also to be credited with pointing out the fact that any coupler curve of a 4-bar mechanism can also be traced by a 5-bar mechanism in which the two cranks are driven in the same direction at the same speed. This is illustrated in Fig. 4.6.

The links shown in Fig. 4.6 with solid lines form a 4-bar mechanism. Point *C* is the coupler point whose path is to be considered. The cognate 5-bar linkage is shown with long-dash lines. It is found as illustrated by completing the parallelograms O_2ACE and O_4BCD. Links 5 and 8 will be forced to be always parallel to sides *BC* and *AC*, respectively, of the coupler triangle. Hence 5 and 8 will always turn in the same direction and at the same speed. If we were to eliminate the 4-bar mechanism and were to drive the 5-bar mechanism by turning the two cranks, links 5 and 8, in the same direction at the same speed, point *C* would trace the same path as in the 4-bar mechanism.

Cranks 5 and 8 could be connected in a variety of ways to ensure their turning in the same direction at the same speed.

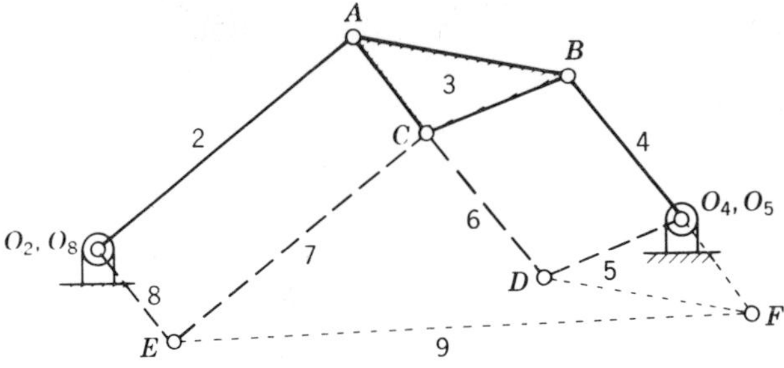

Fig. 4.6 Linkage shown with broken lines will give to point *C* the same path as does the 4-bar mechanism shown with solid lines.

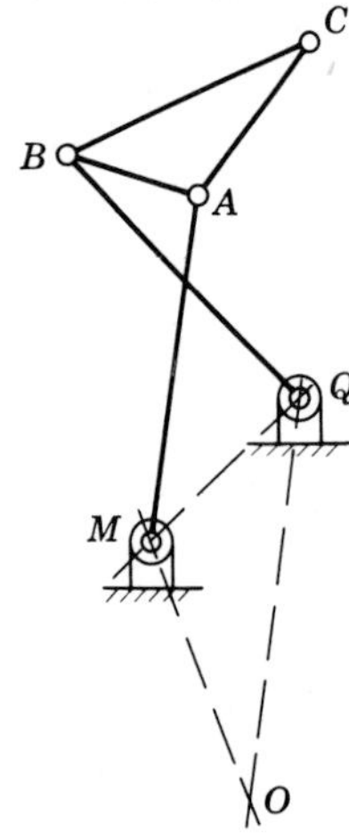

Fig. 4.7 A 4-bar mechanism. Cognate 4-bar and 5-bar mechanisms will be displayed in Figs. 4.8–4.12.

One way would be as illustrated in Fig. 4.6 by the short-dash lines. O_5FEO_8 is a parallelogram. A more practical way to connect cranks 5 and 8 for many applications would be by means of toothed gearing. One example of such a mechanism was described in Chapter 1. We now see the reason for implying there that there was some equivalence between the 5-bar and a 4-bar mechanism.

4.4 *Illustrative problem: finding cognate linkages*

Hartenberg and Denavit (4) suggested the term "cognate" to describe those linkages that trace the same coupler curve. Since there are three cognate 4-bars, to each of which there corresponds a cognate 5-bar, we know of a total of six linkages that will trace identical coupler curves. In this problem we shall find all five linkages cognate to the one shown in Fig. 4.7.

(1) We first construct the pivot triangle *MQO*. This must be similar to coupler triangle *ABC*, with side *MQ* corresponding to side *AB*. The side of the pivot triangle connecting the crank pivots of a particular 4-bar mechanism always corresponds to that side of the coupler triangle connecting the crankpins in the same mechanism.

(2) In Fig. 4.8 we now proceed to find the cognate 4-bar having crank pivots *Q* and *O*. This will be referred to as the "*QO* 4-bar." The original mechanism is the "*MQ* 4-bar."

(a) Complete the parallelogram *QBCD*. *DQ* will be one of the cranks of the *QO* 4-bar and *DC* will be one side of its coupler triangle.

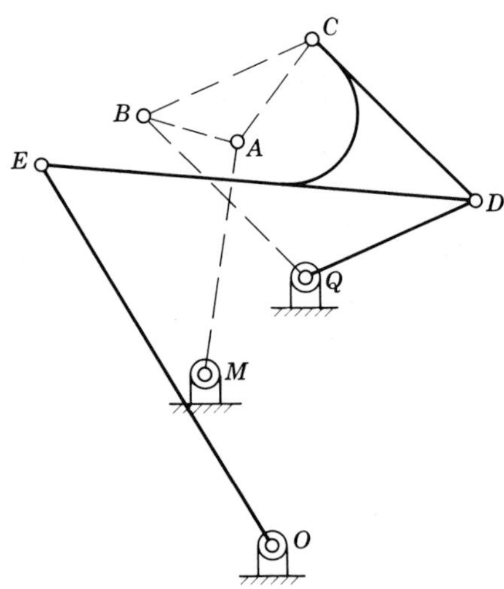

Fig. 4.8 The *QO* 4-bar.

(b) The coupler triangle for the *QO* 4-bar must be similar to the pivot triangle, and the side of the coupler triangle connecting the crankpins must correspond to side *QO* of the pivot triangle. This means that side *DC* of the coupler triangle must correspond to *QM* of the pivot triangle. With this in mind we construct triangle *DCE* similar to triangle *QMO*. *OE* is then the second crank of the *QO* 4-bar.

(3) In Fig. 4.9 the above process has been repeated to obtain the *OM* 4-bar. The coupler triangle for this 4-bar is also similar to the pivot triangle, in this case with side *GF* of the coupler triangle corresponding to *MO* of the pivot triangle.

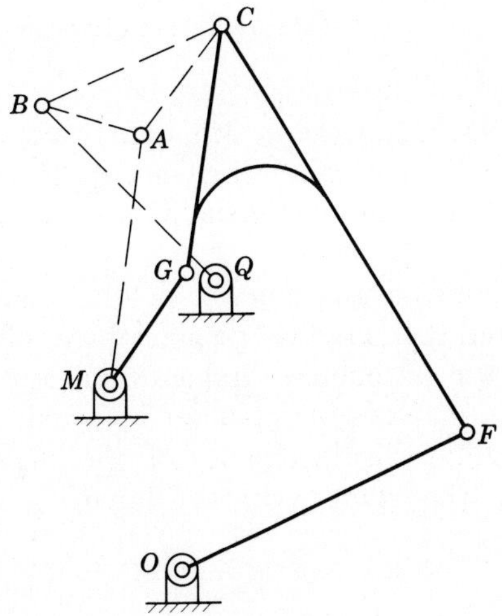

Fig. 4.9 The *OM* 4-bar.

(4) The cognate 5-bar linkage corresponding to the *MQ* 4-bar will be called the "*MQ* 5-bar." It is shown in Fig. 4.10. It should be remembered that this 5-bar by itself is a two-degree-of-freedom linkage. An additional constraint is needed. As indicated in the previous article, the additional constraint must consist of some connection between the two cranks that will cause them always to turn in the same direction at the same speed.

(5) The *OM* and *QO* 5-bar linkages are shown in Figs. 4.11 and 4.12, respectively.

All six linkages displayed in Figs. 4.7 to 4.12 will cause *C* to trace the same path, but there are important differences in other respects. For example, in the original 4-bar (the *MQ* 4-bar) neither of the cranks can execute a complete rotation. In order to trace the full coupler curve, the cranks must be oscillated between their limiting positions. But in the *OM*

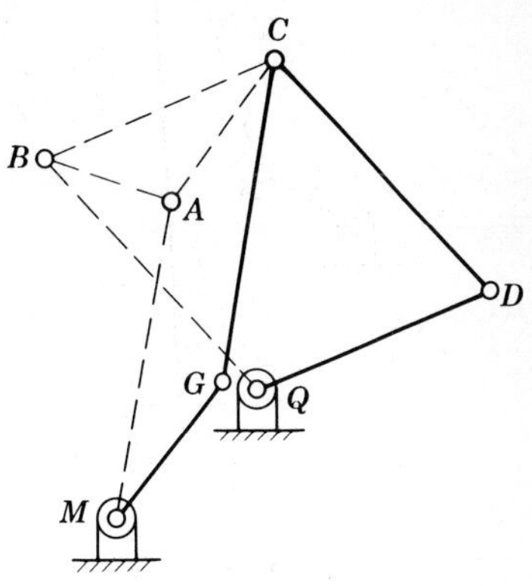

Fig. 4.10 The *MQ* 5-bar.

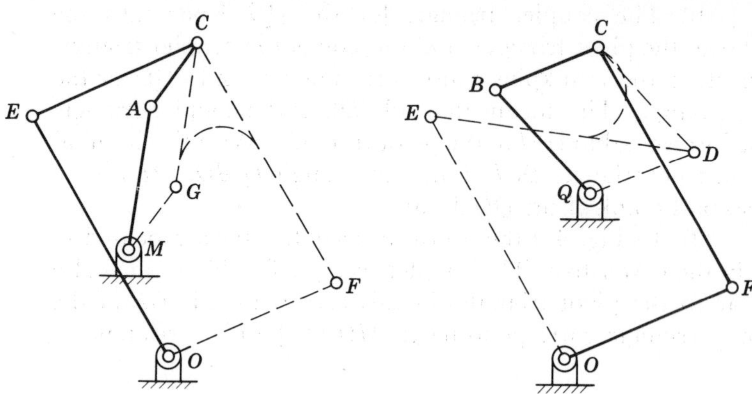

Fig. 4.11 The *OM* 5-bar.

Fig. 4.12 The *QO* 5-bar.

4-bar the proportions are such that crank *MG* can be rotated continuously in one direction. Hence, for an application requiring the full coupler curve the *OM* 4-bar is the easier to drive.

For many applications, displacements of the tracing point, *C*, must be coordinated with angular displacements of the driving crank. Not all of the six cognate linkages will do the same job of coordination. An example of a set in which displacements of *C* and angular displacements of the driving crank *are* coordinated in the same way is shown in the accompanying table.

Mechanism	Driving Crank
QO 4-bar	*QD*
OM 4-bar	*MG*
MQ 5-bar	*QD* or *MG*

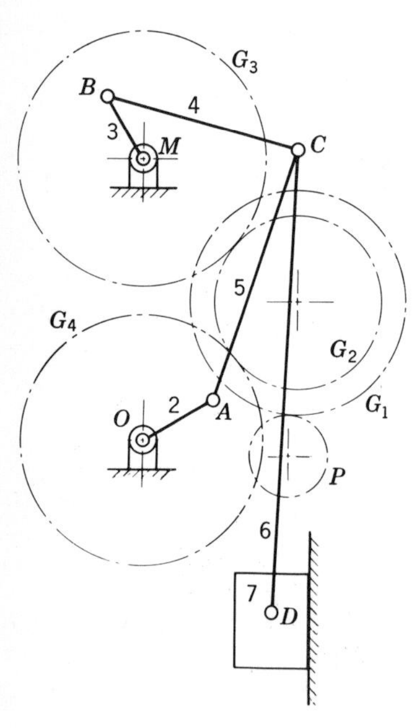

Fig. 4.13 Mechanism of a deep-drawing press.

4.5 *Design problem: press mechanism*

The skeleton drawing of the drive mechanism for a deep-drawing press, originally described in Chapter 1, is reproduced in Fig. 4.13. Links 1, 2, 3, 4, 5 form a 5-bar linkage. The gearing constrains cranks 2 and 3 to rotate in the same direction at the same speed. We recognize, therefore, that point *C* traces a coupler curve.

It is proposed to redesign this mechanism with the object of simplifying it but without changing the displacement-time characteristic of the slider motion.

SOLUTION

(1) From the discussion of the preceding articles we know that among the 4-bar mechanisms cognate to the 5-bar, two

will give the same relation between displacement of C and crank angular displacement as is obtained in the 5-bar. Therefore it should be possible to replace the 5-bar in the press mechanism by a 4-bar. Only one crank of the 4-bar would have to be driven. Hence a considerable simplification in the gearing should be possible.

(2) In Fig. 4.14 we draw the 5-bar of the press mechanism and proceed to lay out the cognate 4-bar having the same crank pivots as the 5-bar. This is done simply by completing the parallelograms $MBCF$ and $OACE$. This 4-bar will not suit our purpose because the coordination between the motion of C and the motion of the cranks is not the same as in the original mechanism. Furthermore, neither crank of this 4-bar can make a complete revolution. What we need is one of the other cognate 4-bar mechanisms.

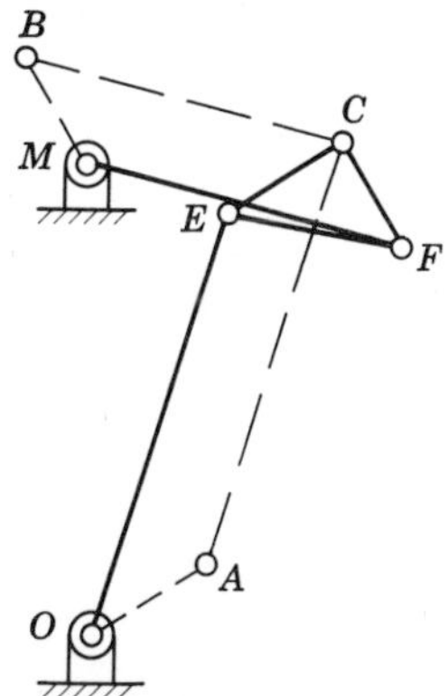

Fig. 4.14 One 4-bar cognate to the 5-bar of the press mechanism in Fig. 4.13.

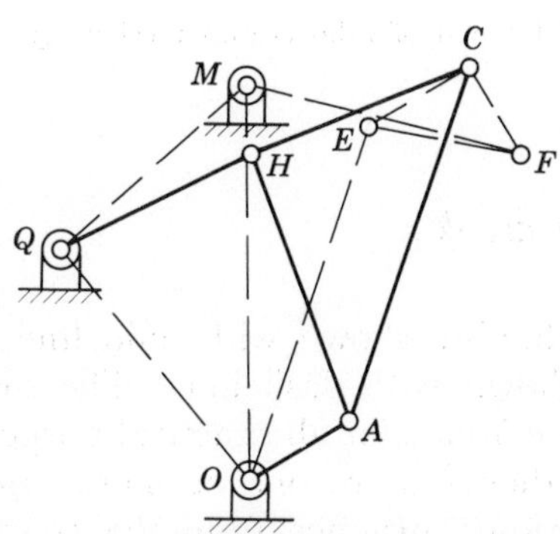

Fig. 4.15 Another 4-bar cognate to the 5-bar of the press mechanism in Fig. 4.13. In this 4-bar the coordination between motion of point C and driving crank rotation is the same as for the 5-bar.

(3) We lay out a second cognate 4-bar as illustrated in Fig. 4.15. In this 4-bar crank OA is identical with crank OA of the original 5-bar. Hence the motion of C will be coordinated with this crank motion exactly as in the original mechanism.

(4) The complete mechanism in skeleton form, as redesigned, is shown in Fig. 4.16. (Links have been renumbered.) This will give the slider, link 6, exactly the same displacement-time characteristic as in the original mechanism.

The new mechanism is definitely better than the old because of the fewer links and gears involved. However, we should not immediately conclude that it is better in all respects. For example, link 3 (the coupler of the new mechanism) will, without doubt, have to be somewhat more massive than the rods of the old mechanism. A final choice between the two mechanisms should rest on an analysis of the dynamics and stresses in addition to the strictly kinematic factors we have considered.

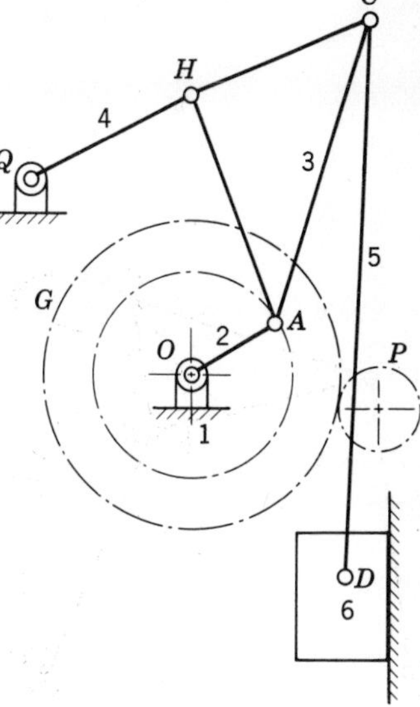

Fig. 4.16 Redesigned press mechanism having the same displacement-time characteristic for the slider motion as in the original mechanism of Fig. 4.13.

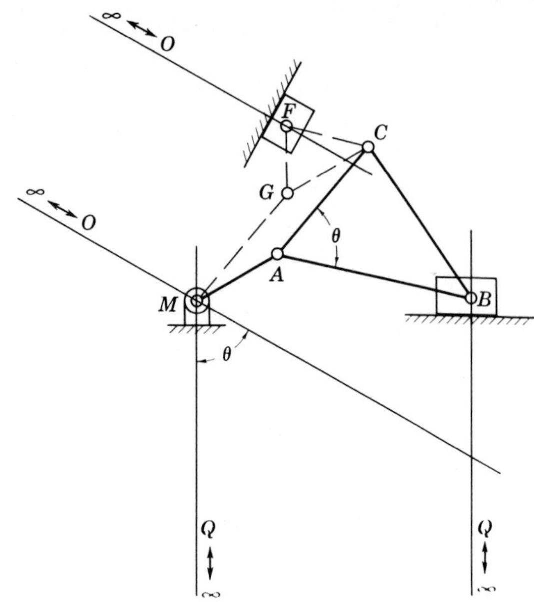

Fig. 4.17 Cognate of a slider-crank mechanism.

4.6 *Cognates of the slider-crank*

The slider-crank mechanism shown with solid lines in Fig. 4.17 has the cognate shown with dash lines. The third cognate 4-bar and the cognate 5-bars for all practical purposes do not exist. Theoretically they require one or more finite-length cranks pivoted an infinite distance from the coupler point *C*.

4.7 *Double points of a coupler curve*

Numerous theorems concerning properties of the coupler curves have been worked out. One theorem having to do with the locations of double points will be stated and proved here.

In Fig. 4.18 is shown a 4-bar mechanism and the pivot triangle *MQO* constructed similar to the coupler triangle *ABC*.

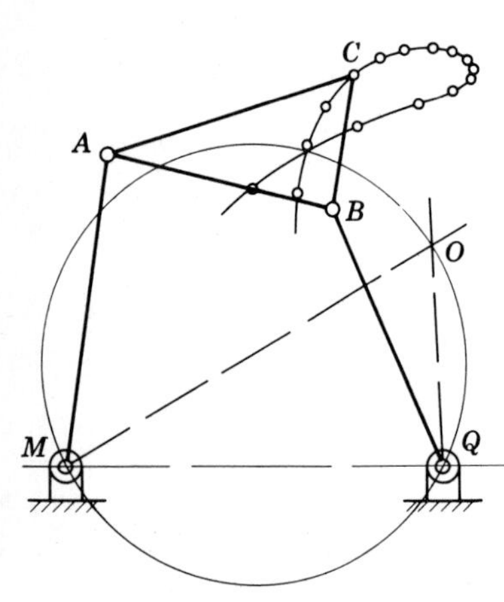

Fig. 4.18 Illustrating a theorem concerning coupler-curve double points.

THEOREM

Any double points in the coupler curve traced by *C* must be located at the points where the coupler curve crosses the circle circumscribing the pivot triangle.

PROOF

(1) In Fig. 4.19 let *ABC* be a coupler triangle with *C* located at a double point of its path.

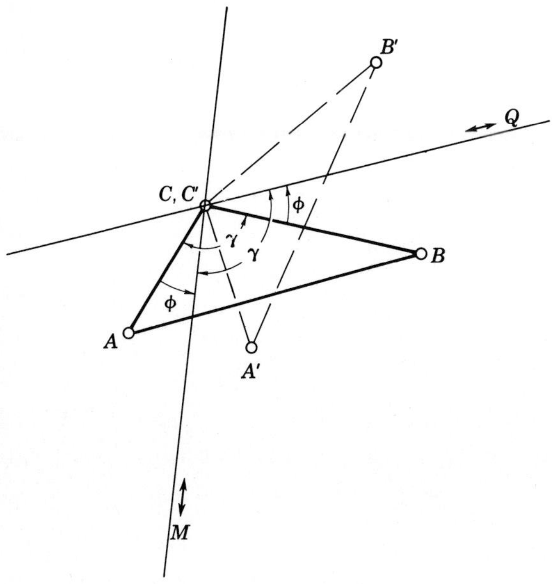

Fig. 4.19 Reference diagram for proving a theorem on coupler-curve double points.

(2) Let $A'B'C'$ be the second position of the coupler for which the tracing point has the same location as C.

(3) The pivot M for crank MA must be located somewhere on the bisector of angle ACA'. Likewise the pivot Q for crank QB must be located somewhere on the bisector of angle BCB'.

(4) It follows that angle MCQ must either be equal to angle ACB (angle γ) or must be supplementary to it.

(5) Hence we conclude that, when a tracing point is located at a double point of its path, it will see the line joining the crank pivots under angle γ or its supplement. The only locations for which this can be true are points on the circle circumscribing the pivot triangle MQO.

4.8 *Coupler-curve atlas*

One very practical approach to some design problems is the use of a catalogue, or "atlas" of curves. *Analysis of the Four Bar Linkage*, by Hrones and Nelson (5), is an atlas of approximately 10,000 coupler curves. Sample pages are shown in Figs. 4.20, 4.21, and 4.22.

The mechanisms whose coupler curves appear in the Hrones and Nelson atlas are all crank-lever 4-bars. Including the cognate 4-bars approximately 30,000 mechanisms are

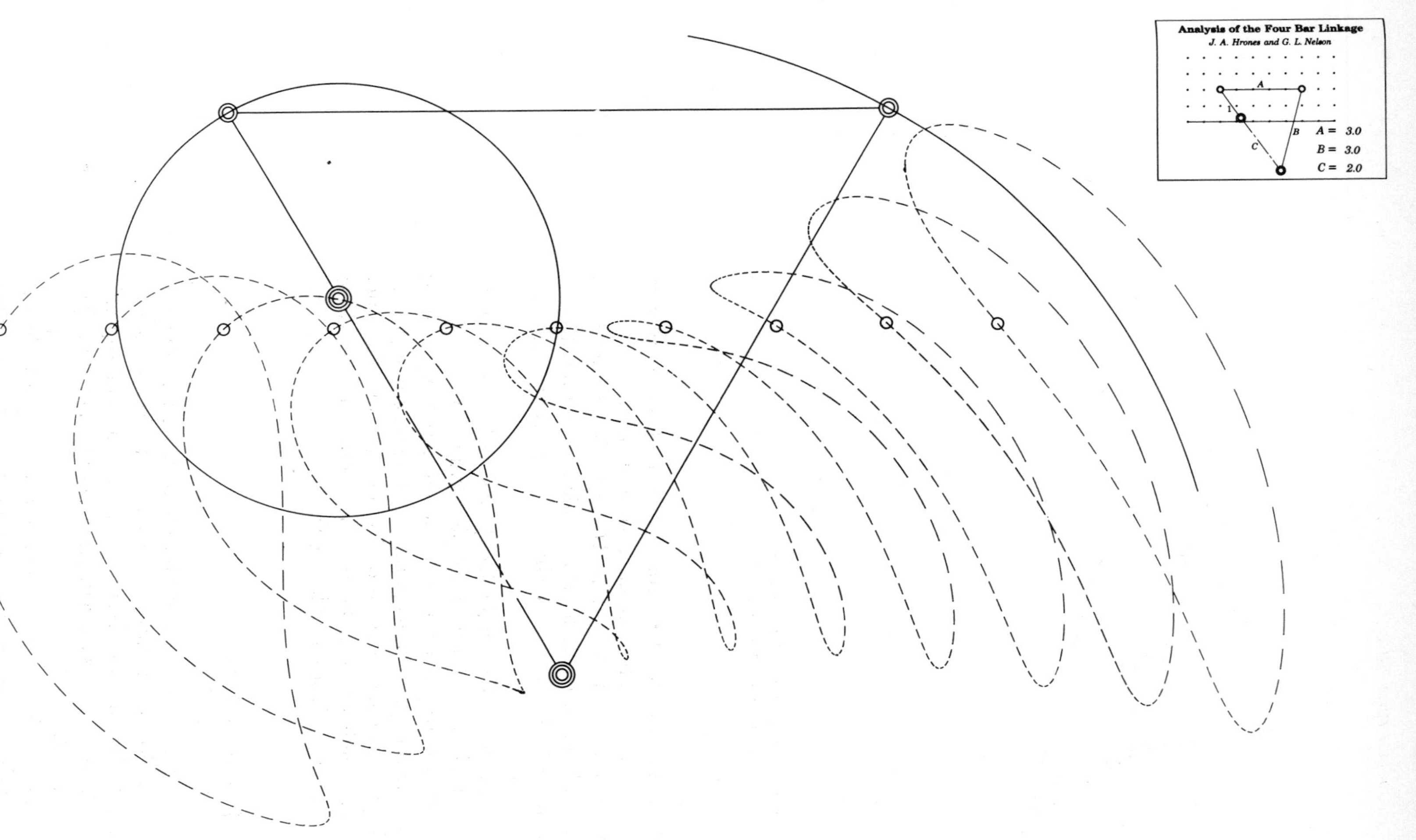

Fig. 4.20 Page 281 from the Hrones and Nelson atlas. Reproduced by permission of the publishers.

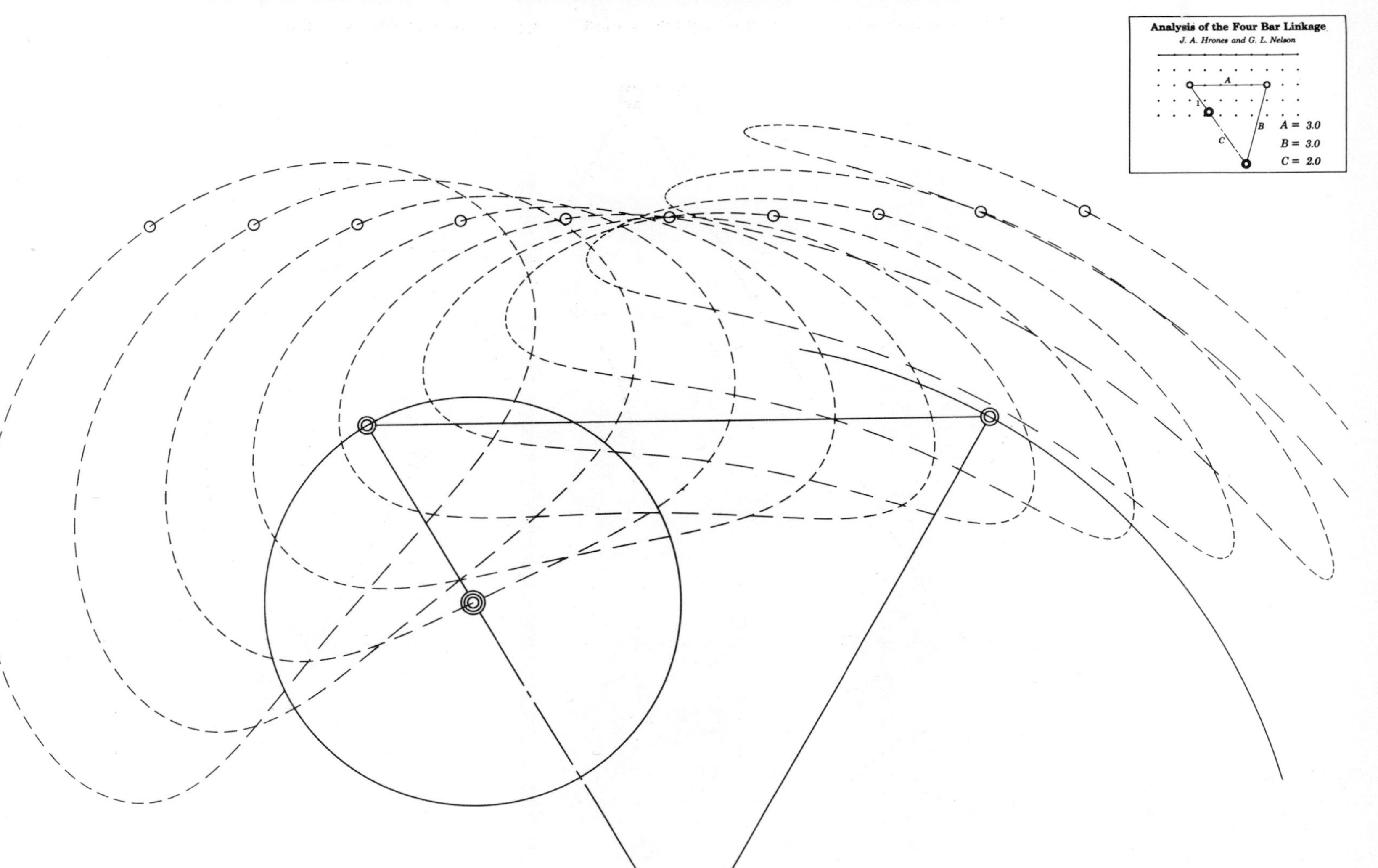

Fig. 4.21 Page 283 from the Hrones and Nelson atlas. Reproduced by permission of the publishers.

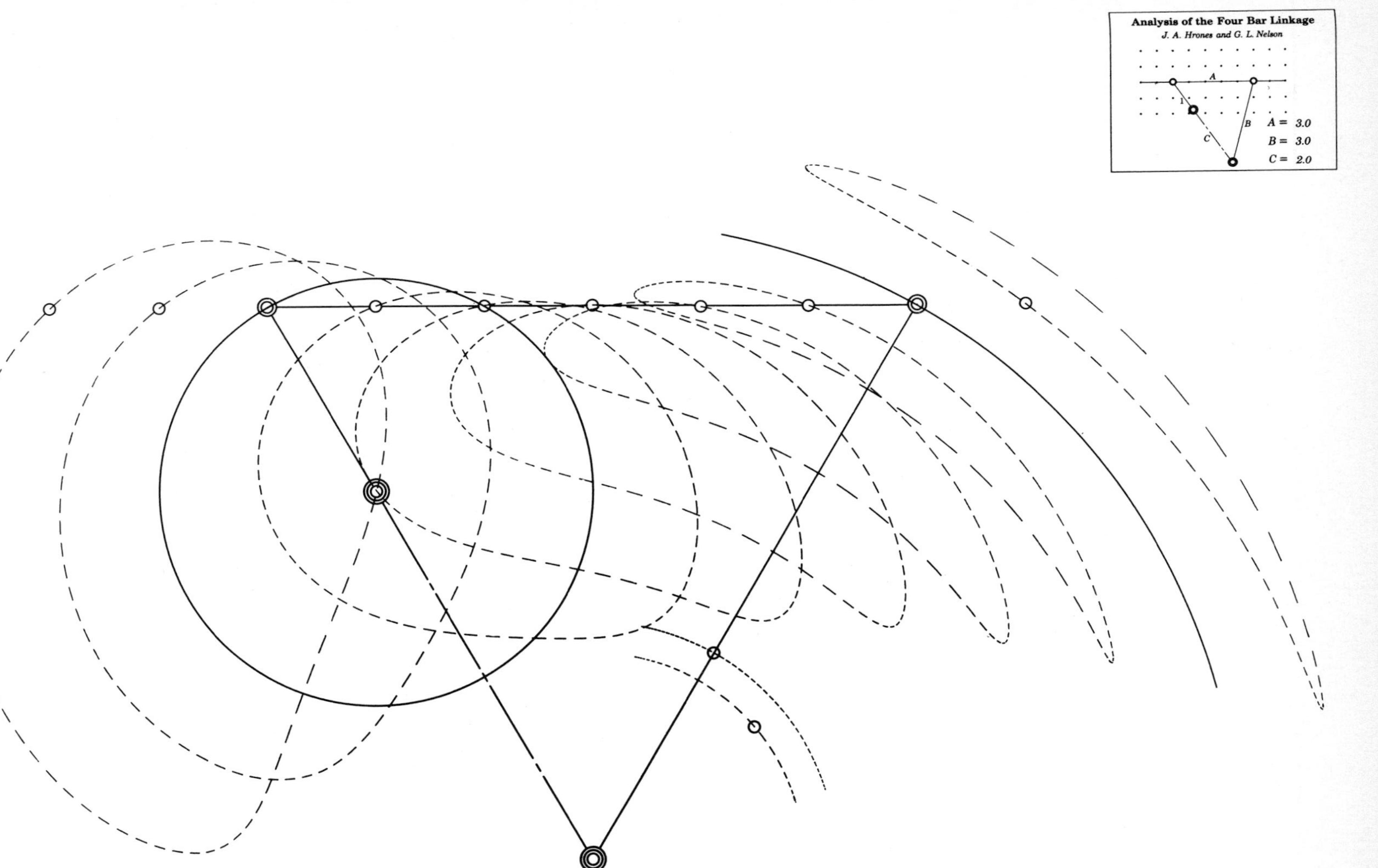

Fig. 4.22 Page 285 from the Hrones and Nelson atlas. Reproduced by permission of the publishers.

represented. However, no drag-link mechanisms are included nor a slider crank in any of its inversions.

Hrones and Nelson have also provided in the atlas a chapter with some discussion and sample design problems.

4.9 *Problem: design of a 6-link mechanism with rotating input crank and intermittently oscillating output lever, with the aid of a coupler-curve atlas*

The mechanism is to have the general form shown in Fig. 4.23, in which link 2 is the driving crank and link 6 is the oscillating output lever. The output link is to oscillate through 30 deg., dwelling in one extreme position while the crank

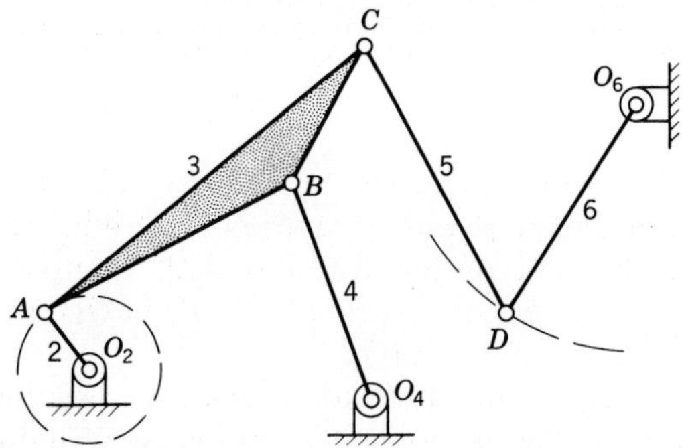

Fig. 4.23 Type of mechanism to be designed in Art. 4.9. Link 2 is input and link 6 output.

rotates 90 deg. The motion of the output link from dwell to the opposite extreme position is to take place during 120 deg. of crank rotation, return during the remaining 150 deg. We shall use the Hrones and Nelson atlas.

PROCEDURE

(1) Examine the atlas of coupler curves. Select a curve of roughly elliptical shape. See Fig. 4.24.

(2) Test the selected curve to see whether a portion in the vicinity of one end of the "minor axis" can be closely approximated by a circle arc. This portion of the curve should correspond to the desired dwell period, 90 deg. of crank rotation.

(3) Repeat steps (1) and (2) until a satisfactory fit is obtained. The curve shown in Fig. 4.24 was the first tested in working up this sample problem and is not the best available.

(4) The radius of the circle arc found in step (2) will be the length of rod *CD* (link 5). The extreme position of point *D* during the dwell period will be the center of the circle arc.

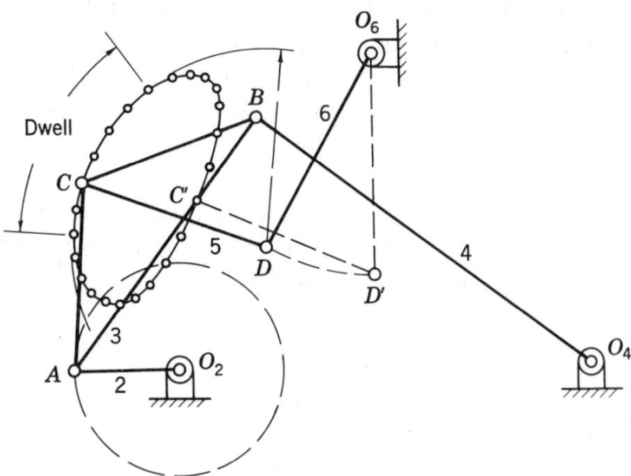

Fig. 4.24 Illustrating design procedure. The dwell in motion of link 6 is obtained by making rod 5 equal in length to the radius of curvature of the path of C and arranging for the extreme position of D to fall at the center of curvature of the path of C.

(5) Point C', corresponding to the second extreme position of the output link, is found by rotating the driving crank 120 deg. beyond the end of the dwell period. Point D' is located on the normal to the curve through C'. Pivot O_6 is found on the perpendicular bisector of DD'.

(6) Plot the displacement of link 6 versus the position of the driving crank in order to display the full cycle of motion. See Fig. 4.25.

In this procedure considerable control is maintained over certain gross features of motion. Whether the design is satisfactory in other respects can be determined only by analysis. For example, if maximum acceleration of the output link is a critical factor, this should be determined, and, if unsatisfactory, other designs should be found by repeating the procedure.

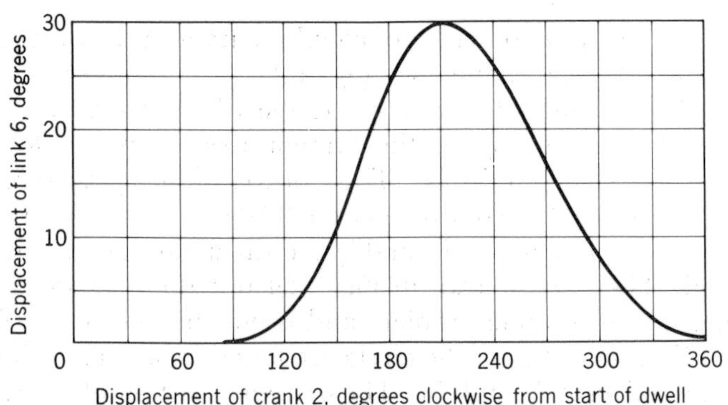

Fig. 4.25 Displacement diagram for the mechanism designed in Fig. 4.24.

Problems and Exercises

E4.1 Derive the coupler-curve equation shown in Art. 4.1.

E4.2 Determine the two 4-bar mechanisms cognate to the one shown in Fig. 4.26.

E4.3 Show one of the 5-bar mechanisms which will trace the same coupler curve as does the 4-bar of Fig. 4.26.

E4.4 Refer to Fig. 4.27. Prove that, if $BQ = BA = BC$, the coupler curve traced by C will be symmetrical with respect to line QC_0. (C_0 is the position of C when A is at A_0.)

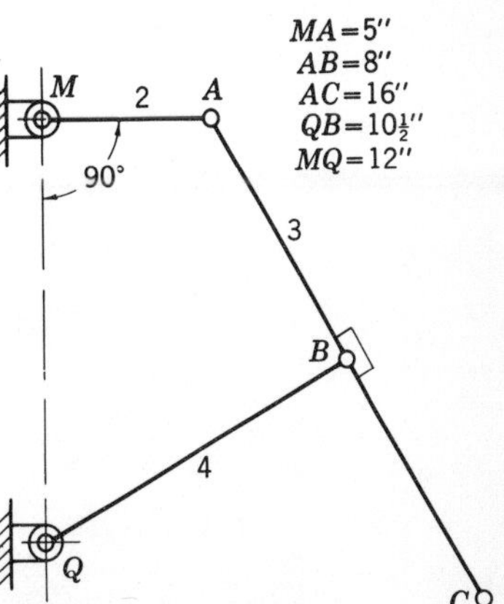

Fig. 4.26 Mechanism of problems E4.2 and E4.3.

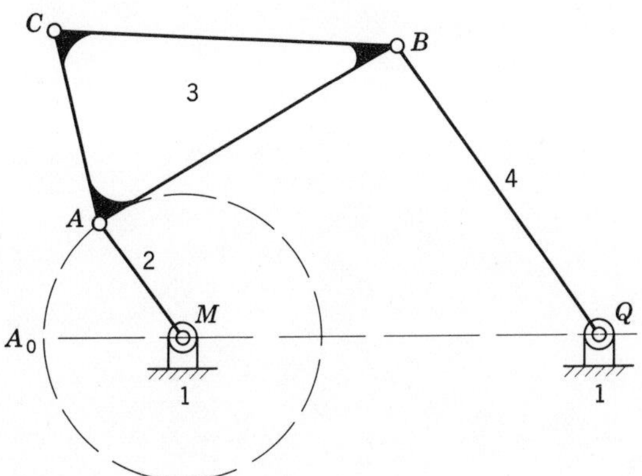

Fig. 4.27 Mechanism of problem E4.4.

E4.5 Design a 6-link mechanism of the type shown in Fig. 4.23 so that the output lever will make two complete 30 deg. oscillations for each revolution of the driving crank. If available, the Hrones and Nelson atlas should be used to select a suitable 4-bar mechanism. (Hint: A "figure-8" coupler curve is needed.)

E4.6 Design a 6-link mechanism of the type shown in Fig. 4.23 so that the output lever will execute the following series of motions during one revolution of the driving crank:

(a) Clockwise 45 deg.
(b) Counterclockwise 30 deg.
(c) Clockwise 30 deg.
(d) Counterclockwise 45 deg.

E4.7 What is the locus of coupler points whose paths contain one or more cusps? Discuss and explain.

E4.8 Both the 4-bar mechanisms cognate to a drag-link mechanism are also drag-link mechanisms. Prove or disprove this statement.

E4.9 Is it possible for one of the cognates of a crank-lever mechanism to be a drag-link mechanism? Explain.

E4.10 Do you agree with the following statements? Discuss and explain.

(a) The cognates of a class I 4-bar are always class I 4-bars.

(b) The cognates of a class II 4-bar are always class II 4-bars.

E4.11 Design a 6-link mechanism of the general type shown in Fig. 4.23 but arranged so that the output link will execute complete rotations. It is required that the output link turn 180 deg. while the driving crank is turning 120 deg., then the remaining 180 deg. while the crank completes its revolution.

5

Path curvature. Inflection circle. Euler-Savary equation

5.1 *Radius vector, radius of curvature, equivalent linkages*

Using polar coordinates, we can write the velocity of a point moving along a curved path (Fig. 5.1) as two orthogonal components,

$$V = R(d\theta/dt) \leftrightarrow dR/dt \tag{1}$$

The acceleration is

$$A = R\left(\frac{d\theta}{dt}\right)^2 \leftrightarrow R\left(\frac{d^2\theta}{dt^2}\right) \leftrightarrow \frac{d^2R}{dt^2} \leftrightarrow 2\,\frac{dR}{dt}\,\frac{d\theta}{dt} \tag{2}$$

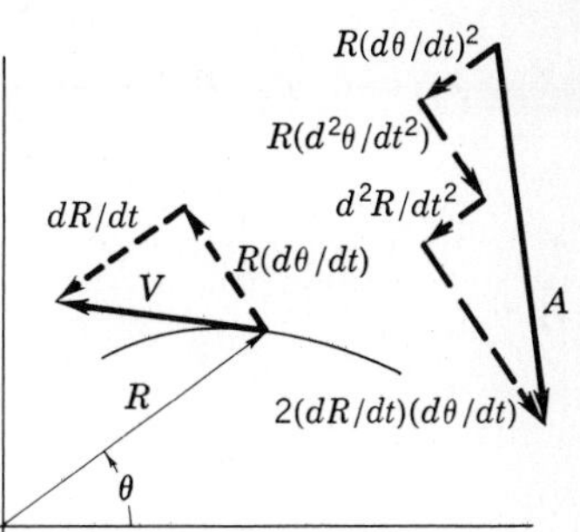

Fig. 5.1 Velocity and acceleration components for a point moving along a curved path.

If, at the instant considered, the origin of the coordinate system is on the normal to the curve through the point (Fig. 5.2), $dR/d\theta$ (and hence dR/dt) will be zero, and the velocity and acceleration expressions become, respectively,

$$V = R(d\theta/dt) \tag{3}$$

$$A = R\left(\frac{d\theta}{dt}\right)^2 \leftrightarrow R\,\frac{d^2\theta}{dt^2} \leftrightarrow \frac{d^2R}{dt^2} \tag{4}$$

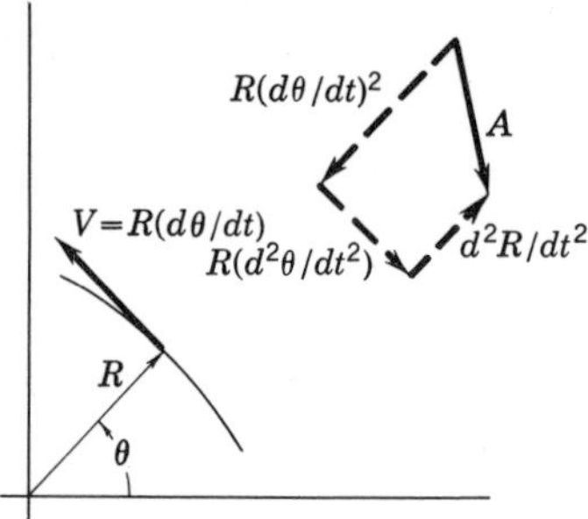

Fig. 5.2 Velocity and acceleration components when the origin of coordinates lies on the normal to the path, through the instantaneous position of the moving point.

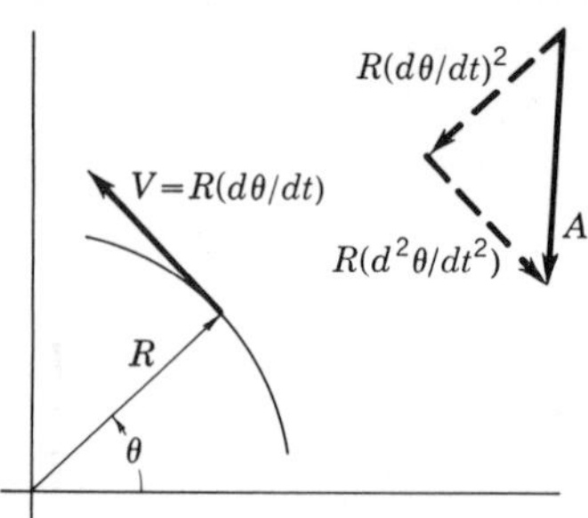

Fig. 5.3 Velocity and acceleration components when the origin of coordinates coincides with the center of curvature of the path at the instantaneous position of the moving point.

If the origin is at the center of curvature (Fig. 5.3), both $dR/d\theta$ and $d^2R/d\theta^2$ are zero (hence d^2R/dt^2 is zero as well as dR/dt), and the velocity and acceleration expressions become

$$V = R(d\theta/dt) \tag{5}$$

$$A = R\left(\frac{d\theta}{dt}\right)^2 \mathrel{+\!\!\!\to} R\frac{d^2\theta}{dt^2} = A^n \mathrel{+\!\!\!\to} A^t \tag{6}$$

One reason for bringing this up is that some of our texts imply that Eq. (6) is correct only if the path of the point is a circle arc and imply that the correct expression for the tangential component for a noncircular path is

$$R\frac{d^2\theta}{dt^2} \mathrel{+\!\!\!\to} \frac{d\theta}{dt}\frac{dR}{dt}$$

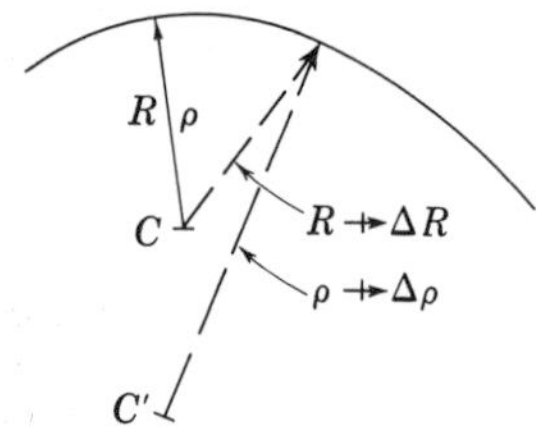

Fig. 5.4 Distinction between radius vector, R, and radius of curvature, ρ.

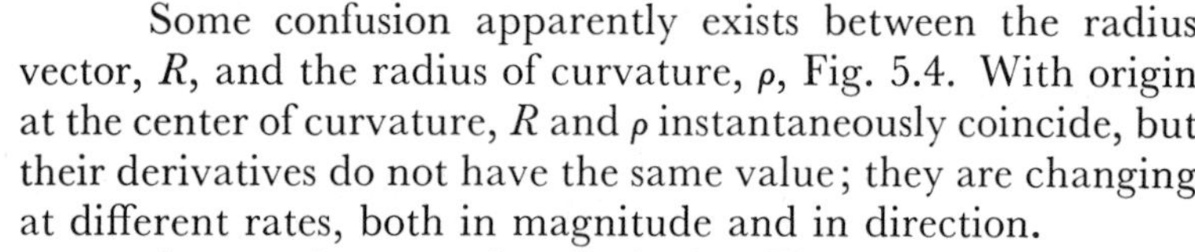

Some confusion apparently exists between the radius vector, R, and the radius of curvature, ρ, Fig. 5.4. With origin at the center of curvature, R and ρ instantaneously coincide, but their derivatives do not have the same value; they are changing at different rates, both in magnitude and in direction.

A second reason for displaying Figs. 5.1–5.3 and Eqs. 1–6 is that they lead us to the matter of "equivalent linkages," a very useful concept. A conclusion we can draw from Eqs. 5 and 6 is that, for the purpose of analyzing instantaneous velocities and accelerations, all curves (paths of moving points or outlines of contacting bodies) can be treated as circles. That is, in our thinking we can replace all such curves by their osculatory circles. We could not do this, of course, if we were analyzing higher derivatives.

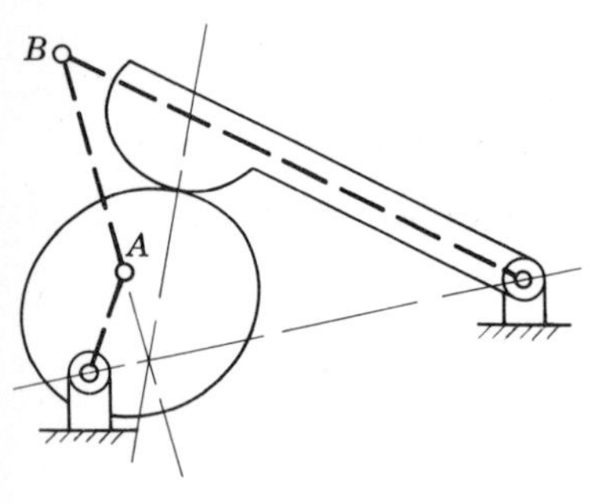

Fig. 5.5 A 4-bar linkage equivalent to the cam mechanism in instantaneous velocities.

For the cam mechanism of Fig. 5.5 there are an infinite number of instantaneous velocity-equivalent 4-bar linkages, obtained by pin-jointing a connecting rod between two points

A and B of the cam and follower, respectively, so chosen that $d(AB)/dt$ will be zero. This will be true for any pair of points A and B located on a line through the common instant center between cam and follower. For the 4-bar linkage to be equivalent to the cam mechanism in accelerations as well as velocities, the points A and B must be chosen so that

$$\frac{d^2(AB)}{dt^2} = \frac{d(AB)}{dt} = 0.$$

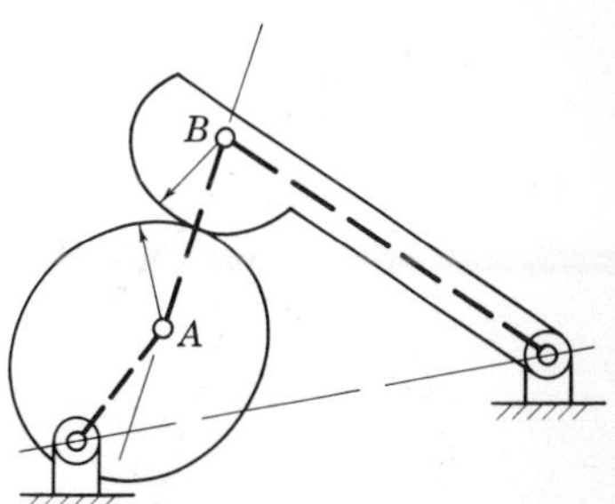

Fig. 5.6 One of many 4-bar linkages equivalent to the cam mechanism in instantaneous velocity and acceleration. A and B are the centers of curvature of cam and follower.

Again there are an infinite number of such linkages, but the one that is most easily spotted is the one which has A and B at the centers of curvature of the cam and follower, respectively, Fig. 5.6. This is usually referred to as *the* equivalent linkage, whereas actually there may be an infinite number of more equivalent linkages, i.e. linkages for which the rate of change of acceleration will be the same as for the cam mechanism.

5.2 *Pole, polode, pole tangent, pole velocity*

The relative plane motion of two rigid bodies is equivalent to the rolling of two curves, usually called the "centrodes." The point of contact between the centrodes is the instantaneous center. Here we shall use the terms "polode" and "pole" in place of "centrode" and "instantaneous center."

Portions of the polodes have been plotted in Fig. 5.7 for motion of the connecting rod with respect to the fixed link of the

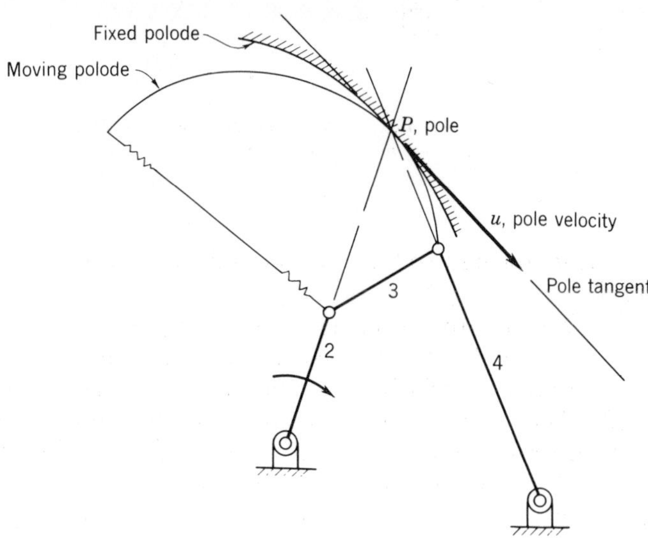

Fig. 5.7 Polodes for motion of the coupler relative to the fixed link in a 4-bar mechanism.

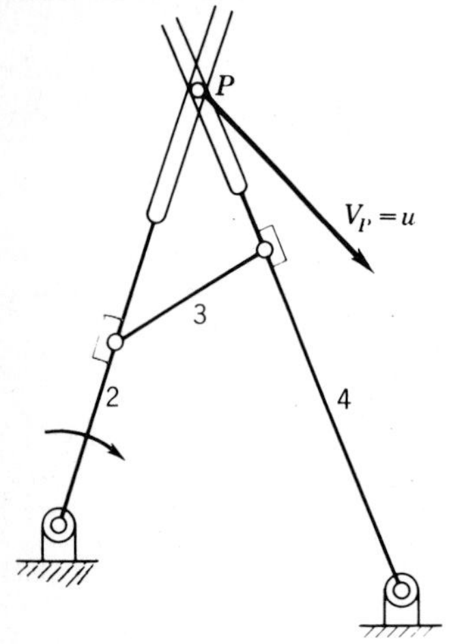

Fig. 5.8 Clarification of "pole velocity."

4-bar linkage. The "pole tangent" is the common tangent between the polodes. The "pole velocity" is the instantaneous velocity with which the pole shifts position. Pole velocity may be clarified by reference to Fig. 5.8, where the cranks of the 4-bar linkage have been shown extended and slotted. A loose pin carried at the intersection of the slots will always be coincident with the pole; the velocity of the pin center is the pole velocity, u.

In the 4-bar linkage of Fig. 5.9 the pole velocity has been determined by means of a velocity polygon. Having exhibited this polygon, we can use it to prove an interesting geometric proposition called "the Bobillier theorem."

The angle between one of the cranks and the pole tangent is equal to the angle between the "collineation axis," PZ, and the second crank.

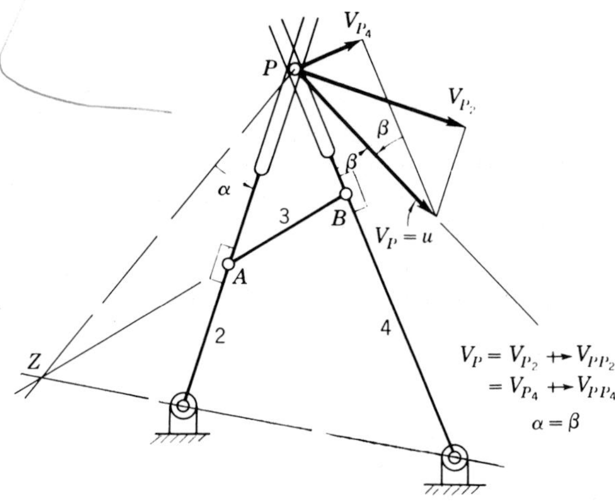

Fig. 5.9 Velocity polygon for determining pole velocity. Also used to prove $\alpha = \beta$.

The following two hints will help the reader to complete the proof.

(1) The relative velocity between P_2 and P_4 is perpendicular to PZ because Z is the instantaneous center for relative velocities between links 2 and 4.

(2) The velocity polygon can be inscribed in a circle.

This proposition is of some use in design as well as analysis, and it is presented here also as an interesting example of the use of *kinematic* analysis to establish a strictly *geometric* proposition.

5.3 *Kinematic analysis for radius of curvature*

The radius of curvature of a point path can be determined from the results of a velocity and acceleration analysis, through the relation

$$R = V^2/A^n \tag{1}$$

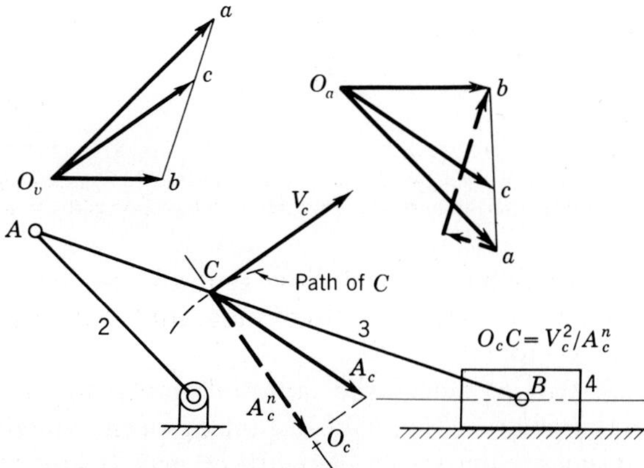

Fig. 5.10 Use of velocity and acceleration analysis to determine the radius of curvature of a point path.

In the example of Fig. 5.10, the velocity and acceleration of point C were determined for an arbitrarily assumed value of the crank speed, ω_2. Since the velocity is tangent to the path of the point, the velocity vector shows us the path tangent and the path normal. The A_c vector is broken into components A_c^n and A_c^t, perpendicular and parallel, respectively, to the velocity vector. Then the distance O_cC from the center of curvature to the point is calculated from scaled values of V_c and A_c^n.

$$O_cC = (V_c)^2/A_c^n \tag{2}$$

5.4 *Acceleration, $-u\omega$, of point at pole*

The point of a moving body which is coincident with the pole has the instantaneous acceleration $-u\omega$, in which u is the pole velocity and ω is the angular velocity of the moving body. This can be derived in a number of ways. One method is to compare the acceleration polygon for A_{p_3} with the polygon for determining the pole velocity, Fig. 5.11. Comparison of the

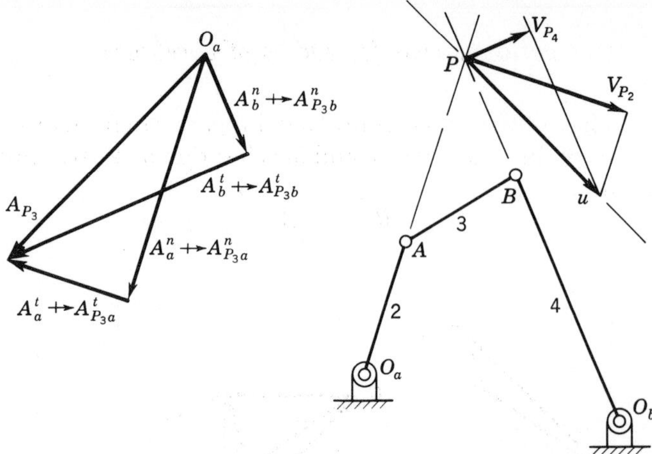

Fig. 5.11 The expression $A_{p_3} = -u\omega_3$ can be derived by comparing the acceleration polygon for A_{p_3} with the velocity polygon for u.

details of the two polygons will show that the two are geometrically similar and that the ratio of magnitudes of acceleration to velocity vectors is ω_3.

Another way to derive the same relation is to consider the rolling of the polodes, Fig. 5.12. Thinking of the polodes as replaced by their osculatory circles with centers O and C, we may consider an extra link, X, pinned between O and C. As is shown in some texts, the acceleration of P_3 is

$$A_{p_3} = A_c^n \nrightarrow A_{p_3c}^n \tag{1}$$

but

$$A_c^n = (V_c)^2/OC \tag{2}$$

$$A_{p_3c}^n = (V_{p_3c})^2/CP = (V_c)^2/CP \tag{3}$$

so

$$A_{p_3} = (V_c)^2(1/OC + 1/CP)$$

$$= -V_c(OP/OC)(V_c/CP) = -V_{p_x}\omega_3$$

$$= -u\omega_3 \tag{4}$$

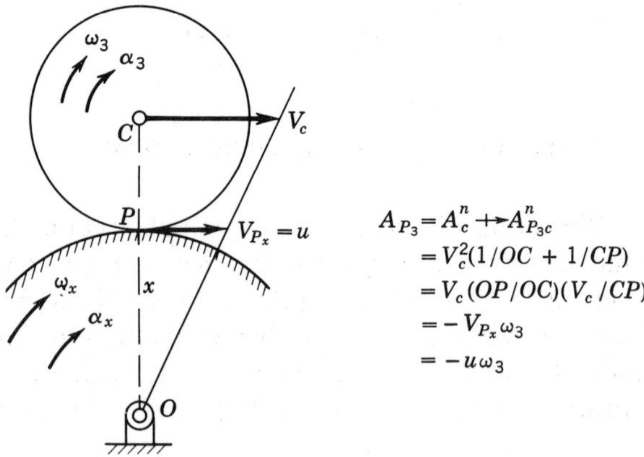

Fig. 5.12 The expression $A_{p_3} = -u\omega_3$ can be derived by considering the rolling of the polodes.

5.5 *Acceleration of any point in terms of the acceleration of the point at the pole, Fig. 5.13*

The acceleration of any point, D, of the moving body can be written

$$A_d = -u\omega \nrightarrow (PD)\omega^2 \nrightarrow (PD)\alpha \tag{1}$$

The normal and tangential components are

$$A_d^n = -u\omega \cos\gamma_d \nrightarrow (PD)\omega^2 \tag{2}$$

$$A_d^t = -u\omega \sin\gamma_d \nrightarrow (PD)\alpha \tag{3}$$

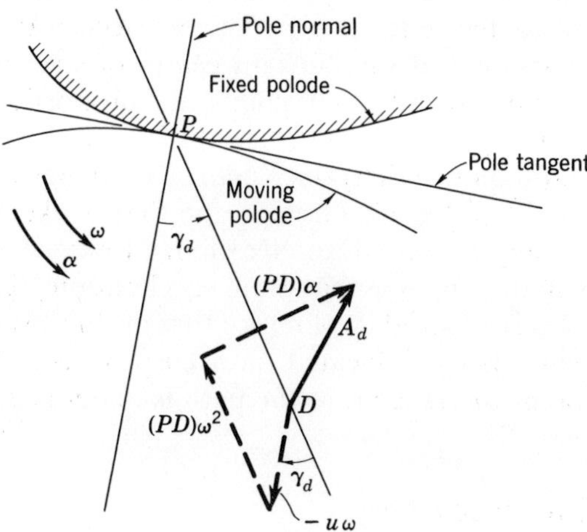

Fig. 5.13 Acceleration of any point, D, in terms of the acceleration of the point at the pole.

5.6 *Points having zero normal acceleration, the inflection circle*

Let J_d be any point having zero normal acceleration. Then, according to Eq. (2), Art. 5.5

$$PJ_d = (u/\omega)\cos\gamma_d \tag{1}$$

This is the equation of a circle of diameter $u/\omega = PJ$, known as the "inflection circle," Fig. 5.14. This circle contains all points having zero normal acceleration, hence points which must at the instant be located on inflection points of their paths.

The point J, called the "inflection pole," has two interesting properties.

(1) The velocity of J is equal to u.
(2) The acceleration of J is zero if $d\omega/dt$ is zero.

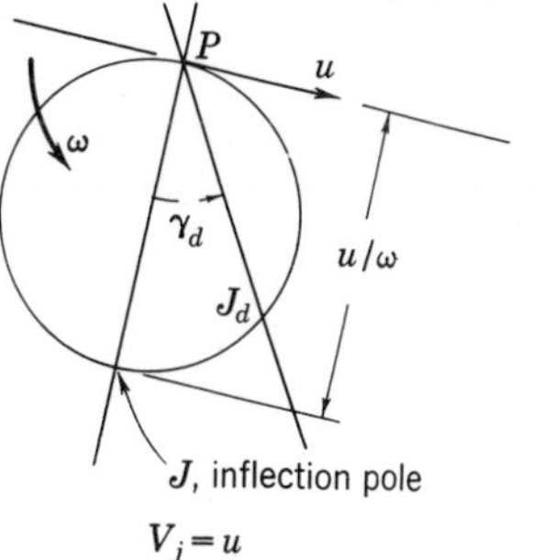

Fig. 5.14 The inflection circle, locus of points having zero normal acceleration.

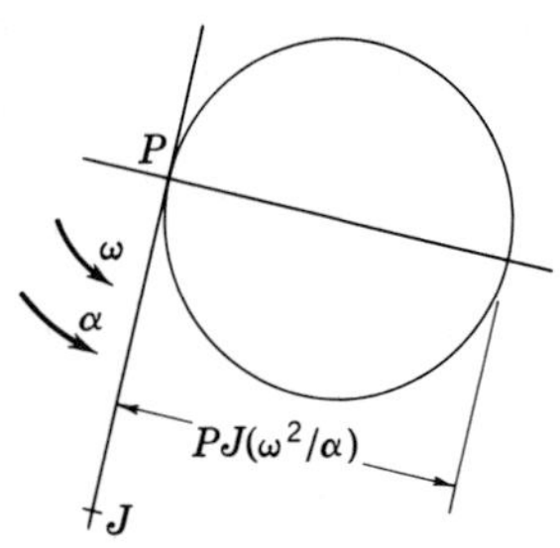

Fig. 5.15 Circle containing points having zero tangential acceleration.

5.7 *Points having zero tangential acceleration, instant center of accelerations*

If we set A_d^t equal to zero in Eq. (3), Art. 5.5, we obtain the following

$$PD = (u\omega/\alpha)\sin\gamma_d \tag{1}$$

or

$$PD = PJ(\omega^2/\alpha)\sin\gamma_d \tag{2}$$

This is the equation of a circle passing through the pole and having one diameter along the pole tangent, Fig. 5.15. Unlike the inflection circle this is not a geometric property of the relative motion; the diameter is a function of (ω^2/α).

In Fig. 5.16 both circles are shown. The intersection point J_0, since it falls on both circles, has neither normal nor tangential acceleration, hence is the point of zero acceleration. This point is sometimes called the "instant center of accelerations." The accelerations of all other points are proportional to their distances from J_0.

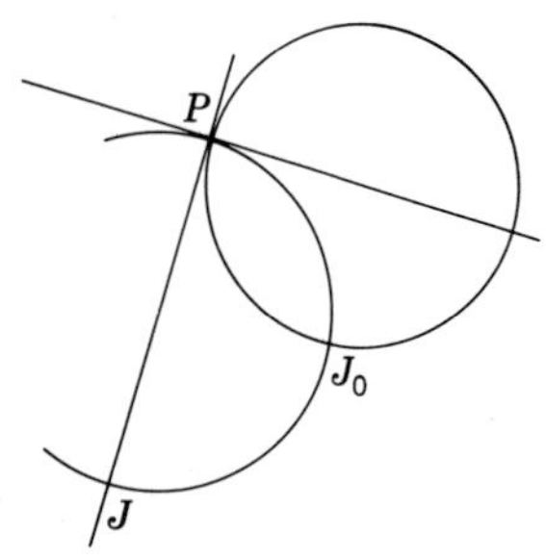

Fig. 5.16 Point J_o, at the intersection of the two circles illustrated in Figs. 5.14 and 5.15, has zero acceleration.

It is of interest to notice that, since point P of the moving body also falls on both circles, we might argue that it likewise has neither normal nor tangential acceleration. However, we have already shown that it does have an acceleration. This seeming contradiction is resolved if we notice that at this instant point P of the moving body is located on a cusp of its path, Fig. 5.17. At this point the tangent to the path is undefined.

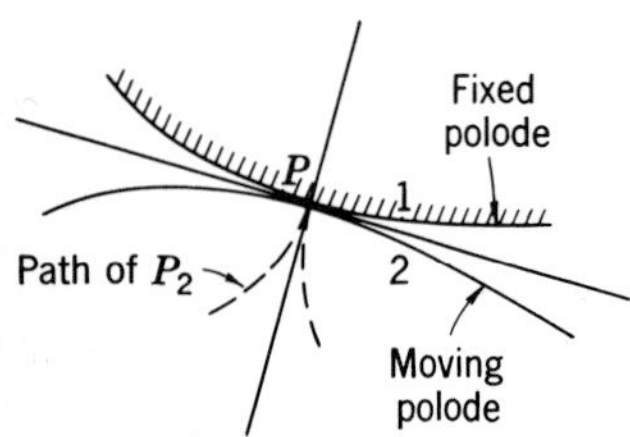

Fig. 5.17 Point P_2 of the moving body is, at the instant, located on a cusp of its path.

5.8 *The Euler-Savary equation*

Referring again to Eq. (2), Art. 5.5, we can use this to calculate the radius of curvature of the path of point D. Let O_d be the center of curvature of the path of D, Fig. 5.18. Then

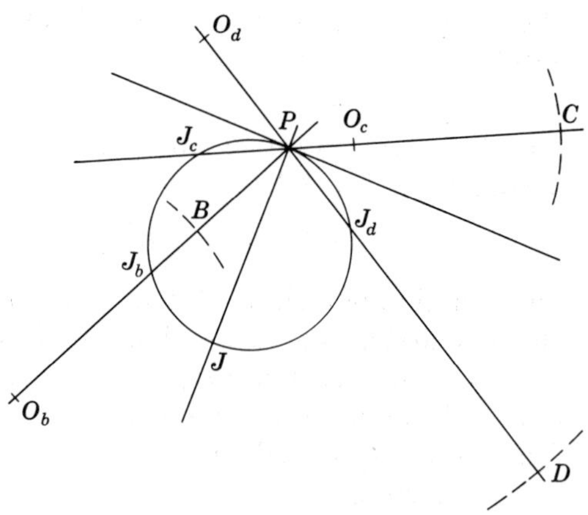

Fig. 5.18 Location of centers of curvature O_b, O_c, O_d for paths of points B, C, D.

$$O_dD = (V_d)^2/A_d^n \tag{1}$$

$$= \frac{(PD)^2\omega^2}{-u\omega\cos\gamma_d + (PD)\omega^2}$$

$$= \frac{(PD)^2}{[-(u/\omega)\cos\gamma_d + PD]}$$

or

$$O_dD = (PD)^2/J_dD \tag{2}$$

This is one form of the Euler-Savary equation. Another form is

$$\frac{1}{PD} - \frac{1}{PO_d} = \frac{1}{PJ_d} \tag{3}$$

5.9 *Problem: inflection circle for a 4-bar mechanism, Fig. 5.19*

Determine the inflection circle for motion of the coupler (link 3) of the 4-bar mechanism in Fig. 5.19.

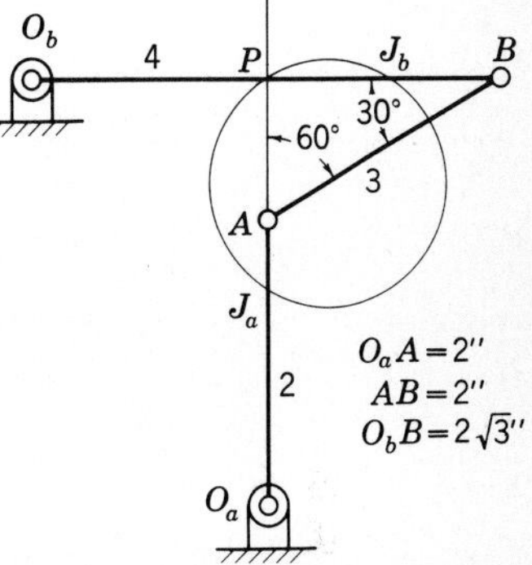

Fig. 5.19 Example of inflection circle in a 4-bar mechanism.

SOLUTION

(1) Find the pole, P.

(2) Point J_b, where the inflection circle crosses the PB line, is found from the Euler-Savary equation

$$J_bB = \frac{(PB)^2}{O_bB} = \frac{(\sqrt{3})^2}{2\sqrt{3}} = \frac{\sqrt{3}}{2} \text{ in.}$$

Point J_b is located to the left of point B. The directed line segment J_bB is always in the same sense as O_bB.

(3) Similarly

$$J_aA = \frac{(PA)^2}{O_aA} = \frac{(1)^2}{-2} = \frac{-1}{2} \text{ in.}$$

(4) The inflection circle is drawn through the three points P, J_b, and J_a.

5.10 *Problem: inflection circle and path radius of curvature, Fig. 5.20*

In the mechanism of Fig. 5.20, determine the radius of curvature of the path of point C in the position shown.

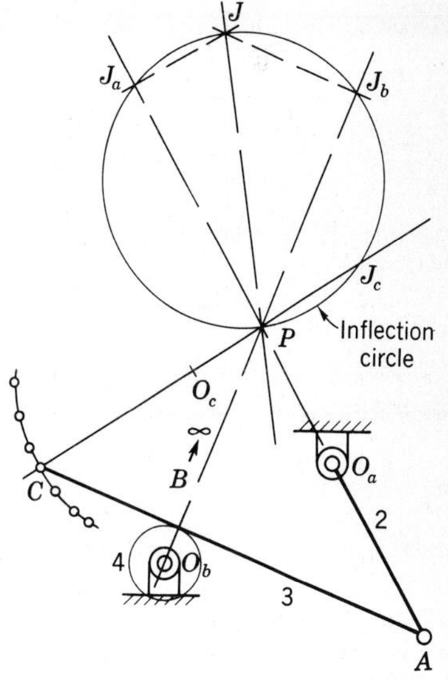

Fig. 5.20 Example in the use of the inflection circle to determine path curvature.

SOLUTION

(1) Locate the pole, P.

(2) The motion of the rod, link 3, is the same as that of the coupler in a 4-bar mechanism, having link 2 as one crank and the second crank pivoted at O_b with crankpin B at infinity along the normal between links 3 and 4. With this in mind we can apply the Euler-Savary equation to find points J_b and J_a on the inflection circle.

(a) $$J_aA = (PA)^2/O_aA$$

(b) $$\frac{1}{PB} - \frac{1}{PO_b} = \frac{1}{PJ_b}$$

but $$PB = \infty$$

so $$PJ_b = -PO_b$$

(3) The inflection circle can now be drawn through the three points P, J_a, and J_b.

(4) Line CP cuts the inflection circle at J_c. According to the Euler-Savary equation

$$O_cC = (PC)^2/J_cC$$

A few points on the path of point C have been plotted as a rough check on the calculated location of the center of curvature.

5.11 *The cuspidal circle, Fig. 5.21*

The inflection circle for motion of body X relative to body Y is of the same diameter as that for motion of Y relative to X but is located on the opposite side of the pole tangent. This can be argued in a number of ways.

(1) The diameter, PJ, of the inflection circle is equal to the pole velocity divided by the angular velocity of the moving body. Hence for motion of X relative to Y

$$PJ_{xy} = u/\omega_{xy}$$

Inverting the motion does not change the pole velocity if the same relative angular velocity is maintained, so

$$PJ_{yx} = \frac{u}{\omega_{yx}} = -\frac{u}{\omega_{xy}} = -PJ_{xy}$$

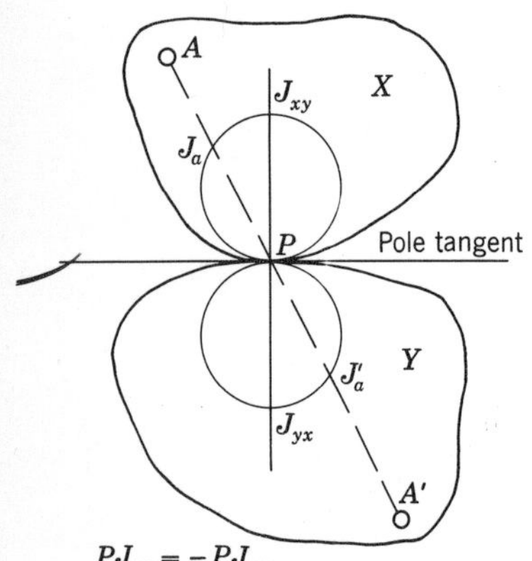

Fig. 5.21 Relation between the inflection circles for motion of X relative to Y and Y relative to X. The inflection circle for one motion is the cuspidal circle for the other.

(2) A second argument can be based on the Euler-Savary equation. Let A stand for any point belonging to body X and A' stand for the center of curvature of the path of A in the motion of X relative to Y.

$$\frac{1}{PJ_a} = \frac{1}{PA} - \frac{1}{PA'}$$

In the inverse motion, A will be the center of curvature for the path of A'. Hence

$$\frac{1}{PJ_{a'}} = \frac{1}{PA'} - \frac{1}{PA} = -\frac{1}{PJ_a}$$

or $$PJ_{a'} = -PJ_a$$

This means that the two inflection circles are symmetrical with respect to the pole.

The inflection circle for motion of X relative to Y is called the "cuspidal circle" for motion of Y relative to X. The name is derived from the fact that a moving straight line belonging to body Y, and located so that it contains point J_{xy}, will have a cusp in its envelope at the second point where the line cuts the cuspidal circle.

5.12 *Graphical solutions of the Euler-Savary equation: the Hartmann construction, Fig. 5.22*

This is a kinematic construction, since it involves velocity vectors as well as distances. Given the pole velocity, u, and the velocity, V_d, of any point, D, first find the component of u normal to the PD line. A line through the tip of this component and the tip of the V_d vector will intersect the PD line at O_d, the center of curvature of the path of D.

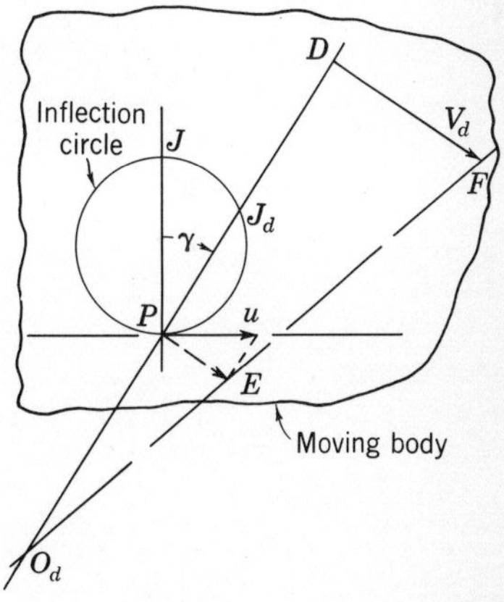

Fig. 5.22 The Hartmann construction.

PROOF

In the construction triangle O_dPE is similar to triangle O_dDF, so

$$O_dD/O_dP = V_d/u\cos\gamma$$

but $$V_d = V_j(PD/PJ) = u(PD/PJ)$$

so $$O_dD/O_dP = PD/(PJ)\cos\gamma = PD/PJ_d$$

Upon substituting $O_dD = O_dP + PD$, the above reduces to

$$\frac{1}{PD} - \frac{1}{PO_d} = \frac{1}{PJ_d}$$

(a form of the Euler-Savary equation previously displayed)

5.13 *First Bobillier construction, Fig. 5.23*

This construction is purely geometric. Given the inflection circle, to find the center of curvature, O_d, of the path of any point, D, first draw a line through P parallel to line J_dJ. This will intersect line DJ at point G. A line through G parallel to PJ (the pole normal) will intersect line PD at O_d.

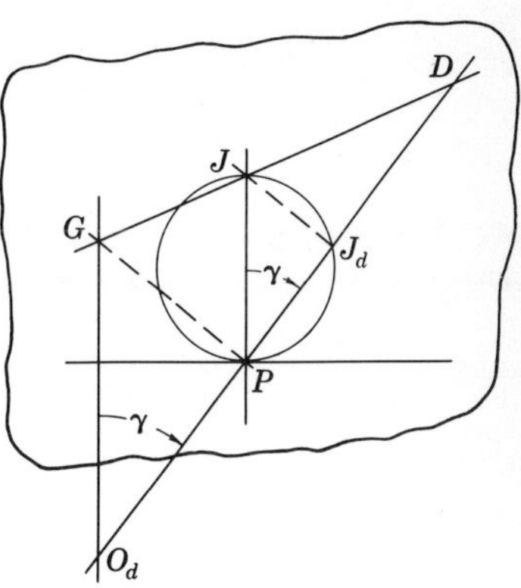

Fig. 5.23 The first Bobillier construction.

PROOF

In the construction triangle DGO_d is similar to triangle DJP, so

$$O_dD/PD = O_dG/PJ$$

but $$O_dG = O_dP/\cos\gamma$$

so $$O_dD/PD = O_dP/(PJ)\cos\gamma = O_dP/PJ_d$$

This will reduce to

$$\frac{1}{PD} - \frac{1}{PO_d} = \frac{1}{PJ_d}$$

5.14 Second Bobillier construction, Fig. 5.24

Given the inflection circle and two points, B and D, of the moving body, to find the centers of curvature, O_b and O_d, of the paths of B and D, proceed as follows.

(1) Draw a line through J_b and J_d to meet line BD at E.

(2) Join P to E.

(3) Through P draw a line parallel to line J_bJ_dE to meet line BDE at Z. (Line PZ is the "collineation axis.")

(4) A line through Z parallel to line PE will intersect line BP at O_b and line DP at O_d.

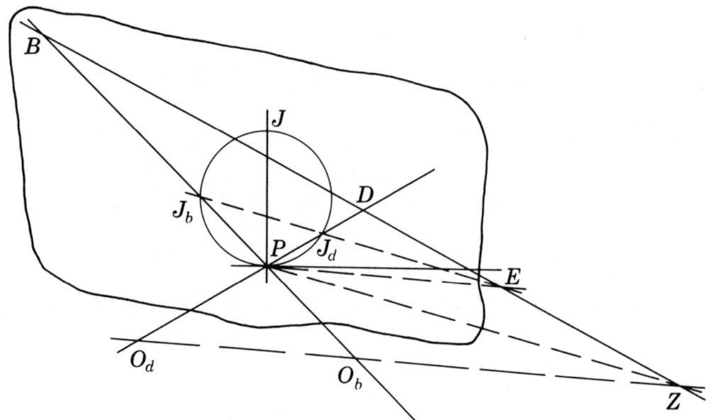

Fig. 5.24 The second Bobillier construction.

PROOF

In the construction, triangle PBE is similar to triangle O_bBZ, so

$$PB/O_bB = PE/O_bZ$$

Also triangle PJ_bE is similar to triangle O_bPZ, so

$$PE/O_bZ = PJ_b/O_bP$$

hence

$$PB/O_bB = PJ_b/O_bP$$

which will reduce to

$$\frac{1}{PB} - \frac{1}{PO_b} = \frac{1}{PJ_d}$$

A similar argument would show that the construction also satisfies the Euler-Savary equation for point D

$$\frac{1}{PD} - \frac{1}{PO_d} = \frac{1}{PJ_d}$$

This construction is perhaps most useful in finding points on the inflection circle when the centers of curvature of the paths of two moving points are known. For example, suppose that it is required to find the inflection circle for motion of link 3 relative to link 1 in the 4-bar mechanism of Fig. 5.25. First locate the pole P, and the point Z, connecting the two with a straight line. Through P draw a line parallel to line O_aO_b to meet line AB at E. Through E draw a line parallel to the collineation axis PZ. This will intersect line PB at J_b and line PA at J_a. The inflection circle must pass through points P, J_b, and J_a.

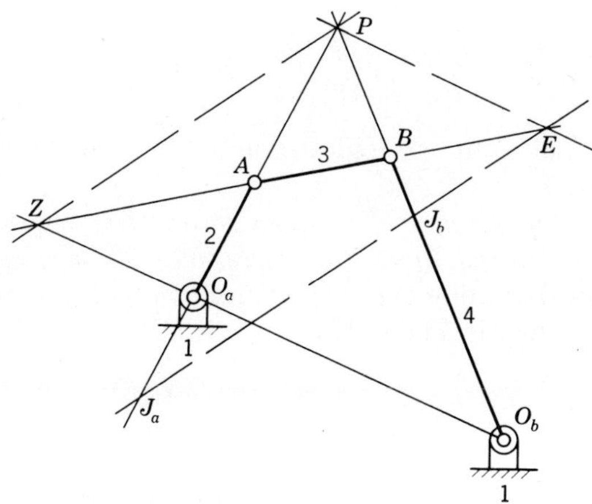

Fig. 5.25 Use of the second Bobillier construction to locate points J_b and J_a on the inflection circle for motion of 3 relative to 1.

5.15 *Problem: determining the radius of curvature of a cycloid*

In general, if we can describe a mechanical means for generating any plane curve, we can find its radius of curvature by application of the Euler-Savary equation. For example, the cycloid (Fig. 5.26) is the path of a point belonging to a circle rolled on a straight line. The circle and straight line are, respectively, the moving and fixed polodes for the motion. The

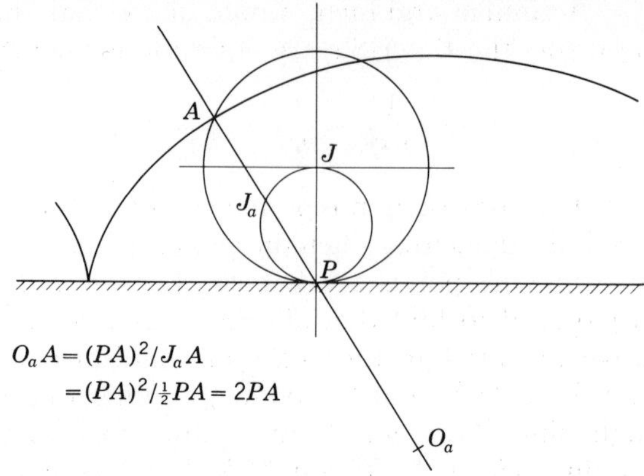

Fig. 5.26 Determination of the radius of curvature of a cycloid by means of the Euler-Savary equation.

center of the rolling circle is the inflection pole, J. At any point A on the cycloid, the radius of curvature is

$$O_aA = \frac{(PA)^2}{J_aA} = \frac{(PA)^2}{1/2\,PA} = 2(PA)$$

Since PA is normal to the cycloid at point A, we can state our result as follows:

The radius of curvature of a cycloid at any point is twice the length of the normal, drawn from that point to the base line.

A graphical solution of the same problem by Hartmann's construction is shown in Fig. 5.27.

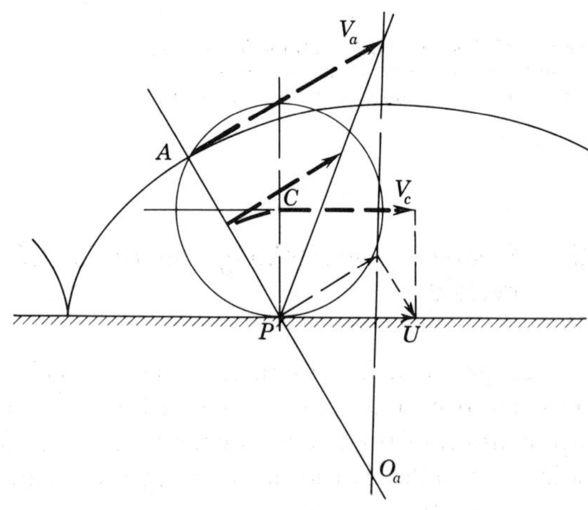

Fig. 5.27 Hartmann's construction applied to finding the radius of curvature of a cycloid.

5.16 *Problem: pendulum period*

The mechanism shown in Fig. 5.28 consists of lightweight links 2, 3, and 4, with a relatively large mass attached to link 3 at M. If properly proportioned, this will behave as a pendulum, with link 3 oscillating each side of the vertical position. This action will be obtained only if the center of curvature of the path of M (in the mid-position) lies above M; i.e., the path of M must be concave upward, else there will be no restoring force when M is displaced from the mid-position.

We shall investigate the mechanism to determine whether it will behave as a pendulum and, if so, what the period will be.

(1) The pole for the motion of link 3 with respect to the fixed link lies at P for the position of the mechanism shown in solid lines. In the mid-position, with M at M', the pole will be at P', coinciding with O_b. The horizontal line through P' will be the pole tangent, and the vertical will be the pole normal.

(2) Point J', where the pole normal crosses the inflection circle, can be located by means of the Euler-Savary equation applied to point A'.

$$\frac{1}{P'J'} = \frac{1}{P'A'} - \frac{1}{P'O_a}$$

$$= 1/3 - 1/5 = 2/15$$

or

$$P'J' = 7.5 \text{ in.}$$

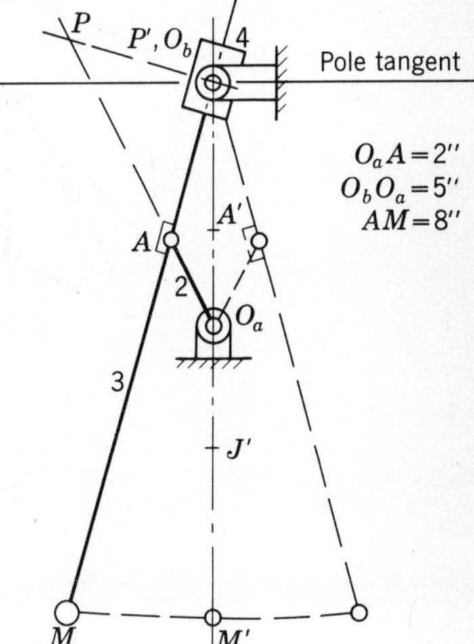

Fig. 5.28 Pendulum problem.

(3) The center of curvature, O'_m, for the path of M in its mid-position can now be located from the following Euler-Savary equation

$$\frac{1}{P'O'_m} = \frac{1}{P'M'} - \frac{1}{P'J'}$$

$$= 1/11 - 1/7.5 = -7/165$$

or

$$P'O'_m = -23.6 \text{ in.}$$

The negative sign means *upward* from P' to O'_m. Hence the path of M is concave upward, and the mechanism will behave as a pendulum, assuming sufficiently low friction in the joints.

(4) The radius of curvature of the path of M is

$$O'_mM' = O'_mP' + P'M'$$

$$= 23.6 + 11 = 34.6 \text{ in.}$$

The period of the pendulum will be very nearly that of a simple pendulum having a length of 34.6 in.

5.17 *Polodes for the relative motion of the cranks in a 4-bar mechanism*

The motion transmitted from one crank to the other in a 4-bar mechanism is the same as that transmitted by a pair of rolling curves, the polodes for the relative motion of the two cranks. Portions of these polodes have been plotted for the mechanism shown in Fig. 5.29. The shapes of these polodes are related

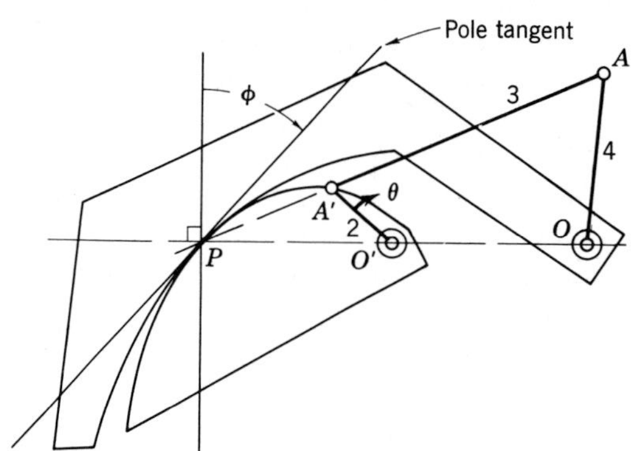

Fig. 5.29 A 4-bar mechanism and portions of the polodes for relative motion of the two cranks.

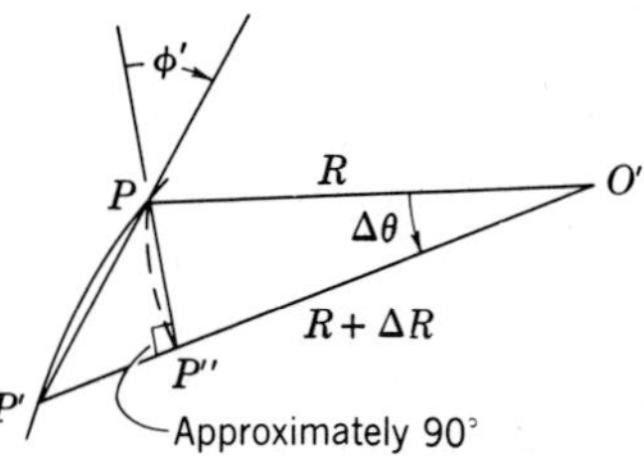

Fig. 5.30 Relation between $dR/d\theta, R$, and $\tan \phi$.

to the angular velocity ratio, ω_4/ω_2, of the cranks, and to how this ratio varies.

$$\omega_4/\omega_2 = n \qquad O'O = l \qquad O'P = R$$

then

$$n = R/(R - l) \quad \text{or} \quad R = nl/(n - 1) \tag{1}$$

Differentiating with respect to θ, the angular position of crank 2, yields

$$\frac{dR}{d\theta} = \frac{-(dn/d\theta)l}{(n-1)^2} \tag{2}$$

but

$$dR/d\theta = R \tan \phi \text{ (see Fig. 5.30)} \tag{3}$$

hence

$$\tan \phi = \frac{-(dn/d\theta)}{n(n-1)} \tag{4}$$

Eq. (4) tells us the slope of the tangent to the relative polodes for a given rate of change of angular velocity ratio with respect to position of one of the cranks.

5.18 *Problem: design of a 4-bar mechanism for specified angular velocities and accelerations of the cranks*

A 4-bar mechanism is to be designed so that, in the design position, with the input crank rotating clockwise at a constant angular velocity of 20 rad. ps, the output crank will have an angular velocity of 15 rad. ps, counterclockwise, and an angular acceleration of 200 rad. ps², counterclockwise. The distance between crank pivots is to be 14 in.

SOLUTION

See Fig. 5.31.

(1) Start a layout by locating pivots O' and O for the input and output cranks, respectively, and calculate the location of the pole, P, for the relative crank motion.

$$R = O'P = \frac{nl}{(n-1)} = \frac{-0.75(14)}{-0.75-1}$$

$$= 6.00 \text{ in.}$$

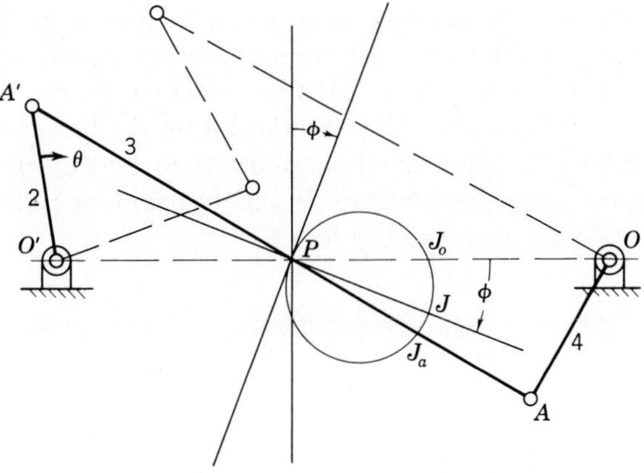

Fig. 5.31 Two different 4-bar mechanisms designed for the same specifications on angular velocities and accelerations of the cranks.

(2) The next step is to find the slope of the pole tangent.

$$\tan\phi = -\frac{dn/d\theta}{n(n-1)}$$

but

$$\frac{dn}{d\theta} = \frac{dn}{dt}\frac{dt}{d\theta}$$

$$= \frac{d(\omega_4/\omega_2)}{dt}\frac{1}{\omega_2}$$

$$= \frac{\alpha_4 - n\alpha_2}{\omega_2^2}$$

However, for this problem α_2 is zero, so

$$\frac{dn}{d\theta} = \frac{\alpha_4}{\omega_2^2} = \frac{-200}{(20)^2} = -0.50$$

and
$$\tan\phi = \frac{+0.50}{-0.75(-0.75-1)} = \frac{8}{21}$$

We can now add the pole tangent to the layout.

(3) We must next establish the inflection circle for the relative motion. Since point O belongs to the output crank, 4, and O' is the center of the path of O for motion of 4 relative to 2, the following Euler-Savary equation must be satisfied:

$$\frac{1}{PJ_0} = \frac{1}{PO} - \frac{1}{PO'}$$
$$= 1/8 - 1/(-6) = 7/24$$
$$PJ_0 = 3.43 \text{ in.}$$

Having the point J_0 located, and knowing that the inflection circle is tangent to the pole tangent, we can add the inflection circle to the layout.

(4) The specifications stated are not enough to determine the design completely. We are now free to choose (a) any slope we like for the connecting rod of the 4-bar we are designing and (b) the location of one of the crank pins on the line chosen. The location of the other crankpin must then be determined from the Euler-Savary equation. If the location of pin A is chosen, then A' is determined as follows:

$$\frac{1}{PA'} = \frac{1}{PA} - \frac{1}{PJ_a}$$

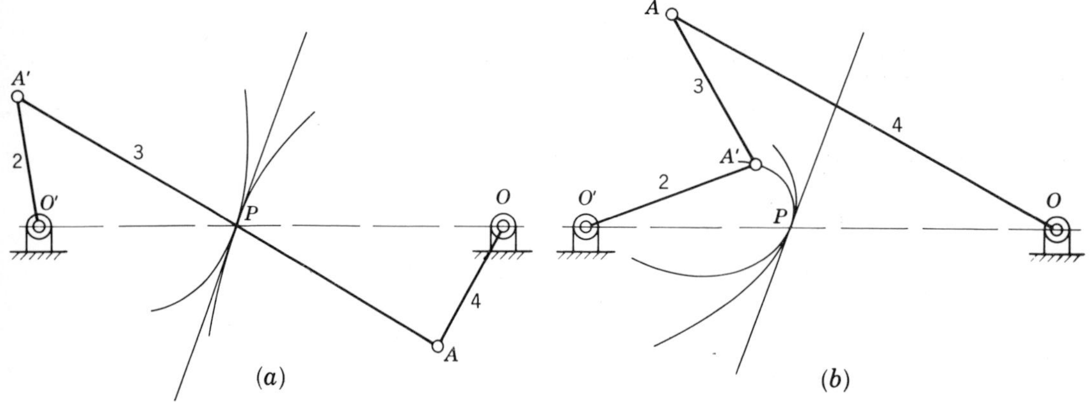

Fig. 5.32 Comparison of the crank polodes for the two mechanisms designed in Fig. 5.31.

Figure 5.31 shows in solid lines the design resulting from one choice, and in broken lines an alternate design. In Fig. 5.32 portions of the polodes for the relative crank motions have been plotted for both mechanisms. While the polodes are quite different in shape, they agree in slope of the pole tangent in the design position.

Problems and Exercises

E5.1 Prove the Bobillier theorem stated in Art. 5.2.

E5.2 Refer to the first paragraph of Art. 5.4. Complete the proof that $A_{p_3} = -u\omega_3$.

E5.3 Prove that the acceleration of any point, D, on a body in plane motion is

$$A_d = (PD)\alpha \nrightarrow (JD)\omega^2$$

where P is the pole, J is the inflection pole, ω is the angular velocity, and α is the angular acceleration of the body.

E5.4 The radii of curvature of the paths of two points, A and B, belonging to the same rigid body in plane motion and located on the same line through the pole, P, are related by the following expression:

$$O_bB = O_aA(PB/PA)(PO_b/PO_a)$$

Prove this.

E5.5 Consider a body in plane motion. Let D stand for the diameter of the inflection circle and ρ for the radius of curvature of a point path. Derive the equation for the locus of all points for which $|\rho/D| = k$, where k is any constant. The equation should be put in the form

$$r/D = \mathrm{f}(k, \gamma)$$

where r is the distance from the pole to the moving point and γ is the angle from the pole normal.

E5.6 Draw a conventional (not offset) slider-crank mechanism having a crank length of 2 in., rod length of 6 in., with the crank at an angle of 135 deg. from head-end dead center.

(a) Determine the inflection circle for motion of the rod relative to the fixed link.

(b) Determine the radius of curvature of the path of the mid-point of the rod.

E5.7 Show that the center of curvature for the path which A_3 traces with respect to link 2 in Fig. 5.33 is located exactly midway between Z and A.

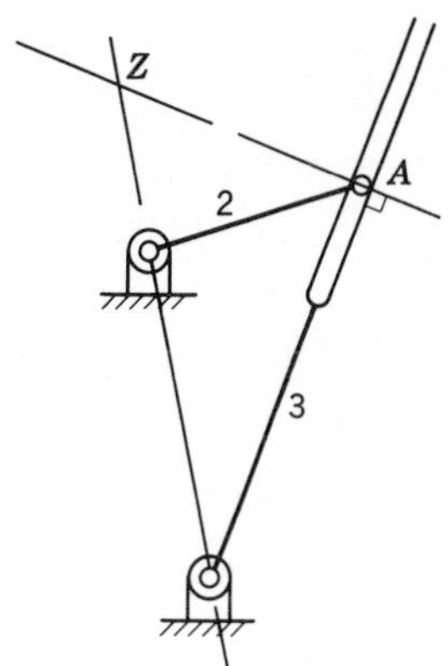

Fig. 5.33 Mechanism for problem E5.7.

E5.8 By application of the Euler-Savary equation, find the center of curvature of the path which A_3 traces with respect to link 2 in Fig. 5.34.

E5.9 Lay out a 4-bar mechanism and find the inflection and cuspidal circles for motion of the coupler with respect to the fixed link. Choose a straight line so located that it cuts the cuspidal circle at the opposite end of the diameter through P and at one other point.

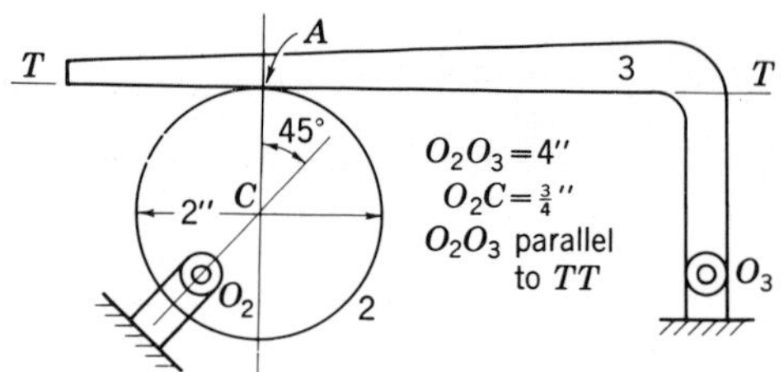

Fig. 5.34 Mechanism for problem E5.8.

Considering this line as a part of the coupler, draw several positions each side of the initial position. Draw the envelope of this moving line. According to Art. 5.11, this envelope should have a cusp at the initial position of the line.

E5.10 Describe a mechanism which will generate ellipses. Show how the Euler-Savary equation can be applied to the problem of determining the radius of curvature of an ellipse at any point.

E5.11 The symmetrical 4-bar linkage shown in Fig. 5.35 is suspended from a fixed pivot, E, at the mid-point of link 2. Links 2, 3, and 5 are relatively light in weight, but link 4 is heavy, with center of gravity at G. Determine whether the configuration is stable; i.e., would the linkage return to the position shown after a small displacement? Neglect friction in the joints. If you find that it is stable,

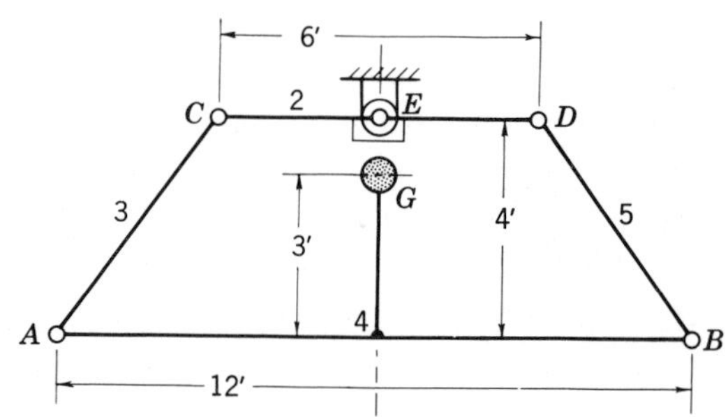

Fig. 5.35 Mechanism for problem E5.11.

state the maximum height possible for G above line AB without destroying the stability. If you find that it is unstable, state how far G would have to be lowered to achieve stability.

E5.12 Prove that, in any 4-bar mechanism, the angular velocity ratio of the cranks is either a maximum or a minimum when the collineation axis is normal to the connecting rod.

E5.13 Design a 4-bar mechanism so that the angular velocity ratio, n, of the cranks in the design position will be $+1.5$, and so that the angular acceleration of the output crank will be zero if the angular acceleration of the input crank is zero.

6

Polode curvature. The cubic of stationary curvature

6.1 *Polode radii of curvature*

The radius of curvature, R_f, of the fixed polode can be determined if we know the pole velocity, u, and the corresponding pole acceleration, A_p.

$$R_f = u^2/A_p^n \tag{1}$$

The sketch, Fig. 6.1, shows a 4-bar mechanism and a vector diagram for determining the acceleration A_p. It has been assumed that the pole velocity, u, is already known and that the angular acceleration, α_3, of the coupler is zero. The pole acceleration, A_p can be written

$$A_p = A_{p_2} \leftrightarrow A_{pp_2}$$

$$= A_{p_2} \leftrightarrow 2V_{pp_2}\,\omega_2 \leftrightarrow a^t_{pp_2}$$

but $$A_{p_2} = A_a(O_aP/O_aA)$$

and $$A_a = -u\omega_3 \leftrightarrow A^n_{ap_3}$$

hence $$A_p = -u\omega_3\frac{O_aP}{O_aA} \leftrightarrow 2V_{pp_2}\,\omega_2 \leftrightarrow \left[A^n_{ap_2}\frac{O_aP}{O_aA} + a^t_{pp_2}\right] \tag{2}$$

Similarly $A_p = -u\omega_3 \dfrac{O_bP}{O_bB} \nrightarrow 2V_{pp_4}\omega_4 \nrightarrow \left[A^n_{bp_3}\dfrac{O_bP}{O_bB} + a^t_{pp_4}\right]$ (3)

The simultaneous solution of Eqs. (2) and (3) for A_p is shown in Fig. 6.1. For greater clarity, a portion of the acceleration vector diagram has been shown again in Fig. 6.2. From examination of this sketch

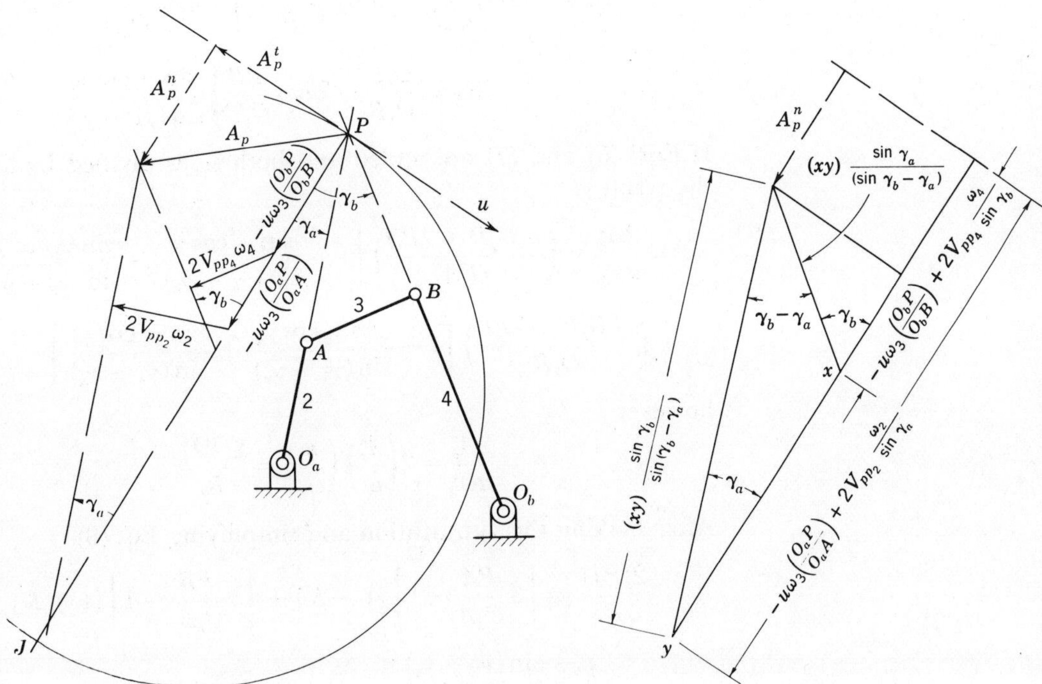

Fig. 6.1 Sketch of vector polygon for determining A_p.

Fig. 6.2 Part of vector diagram from Fig. 6.1.

$$A^n_p = -u\omega_3\frac{O_aP}{O_aA} + \frac{2V_{pp_2}\omega_2}{\sin\gamma_a} - \left[-u\omega_3\frac{O_aP}{O_aA} + \frac{2V_{pp_2}\omega_2}{\sin\gamma_a} + u\omega_3\frac{O_bP}{O_bB} - \frac{2V_{pp_4}\omega_4}{\sin\gamma_b}\right]\frac{\sin\gamma_b\cos\gamma_a}{\sin(\gamma_b-\gamma_a)} \quad (4)$$

also

$$A^n_p = -u\omega_3\frac{O_bP}{O_bB} + \frac{2V_{pp_4}\omega_4}{\sin\gamma_b} - \left[-u\omega_3\frac{O_aP}{O_aA} + \frac{2V_{pp_2}\omega_2}{\sin\gamma_a} + u\omega_3\frac{O_bP}{O_bB} - \frac{2V_{pp_4}\omega_4}{\sin\gamma_b}\right]\frac{\sin\gamma_a\cos\gamma_b}{\sin(\gamma_b-\gamma_a)} \quad (5)$$

In these equations the following substitutions may be made:

$$V_{pp_2} = u\sin\gamma_a \qquad V_{pp_4} = u\sin\gamma_b$$
$$\omega_2 = \omega_3(PA/O_aA) \qquad \omega_4 = \omega_3(PB/O_bB)$$

The result is

$$A_p^n = -u\omega_3\frac{O_aP}{O_aA} + 2u\omega_3\frac{PA}{O_aA} - \left[-u\omega_3\frac{O_aP}{O_aA} + 2u\omega_3\frac{PA}{O_aA}\right.$$

$$\left. + u\omega_3\frac{O_bP}{O_bB} - 2u\omega_3\frac{PB}{O_bB}\right]\frac{\sin\gamma_b\cos\gamma_a}{\sin(\gamma_b-\gamma_a)} \tag{6}$$

and

$$A_p^n = -u\omega_3\frac{O_bP}{O_bB} + 2u\omega_3\frac{PB}{O_bB} - \left[-u\omega_3\frac{O_aP}{O_aA} + 2u\omega_3\frac{PA}{O_aA}\right.$$

$$\left. + u\omega_3\frac{O_bP}{O_bB} - 2u\omega_3\frac{PB}{O_bB}\right]\frac{\sin\gamma_a\cos\gamma_b}{\sin(\gamma_b-\gamma_a)} \tag{7}$$

If Eqs. (6) and (7) are added and both sides divided by $u\omega_3$, the result is

$$\frac{2A_p^n}{u\omega_3} = \left(\frac{-O_aP + 2PA}{O_aA}\right)\left[1 - \frac{\sin\gamma_b\cos\gamma_a}{\sin(\gamma_b-\gamma_a)} - \frac{\sin\gamma_a\cos\gamma_b}{\sin(\gamma_b-\gamma_a)}\right]$$

$$+\left(\frac{-O_bP + 2PB}{O_bB}\right)\left[1 + \frac{\sin\gamma_b\cos\gamma_a}{\sin(\gamma_b-\gamma_a)} + \frac{\sin\gamma_a\cos\gamma_b}{\sin(\gamma_b-\gamma_a)}\right] \tag{8}$$

however

$$\frac{2A_p^n}{u\omega_3} = 2\left(\frac{A_p^n}{u^2}\right)\left(\frac{u}{\omega_3}\right) = \frac{2(PJ)}{R_f}$$

After making this substitution and simplifying Eq. (8)

$$\frac{2(PJ)}{R_f} = \left[3\frac{PA}{O_aA} - 1\right](1-K) + \left[3\frac{PB}{O_bB} - 1\right](1+K)$$

$$K = \frac{\sin(\gamma_b+\gamma_a)}{\sin(\gamma_b-\gamma_a)} \tag{9}$$

Rules for signs: positive directions, P to A, P to B, P to J. For positive R_f the center of curvature of the polode is located on the side of P away from J. [Students should check these rules, as well as the numerical results of Eq. (9), for several different cases.]

6.2 *Problem: determining the radii of curvature of polodes in a 4-bar mechanism*

The radii of curvature of the polodes for motion of the coupler relative to the fixed link are to be determined for the mechanism shown in Fig. 6.3.

(1) Calculate the location of point J_a on the inflection circle.

$$\frac{1}{PJ_a} = \frac{1}{PA} - \frac{1}{PO_a} = \frac{1}{PA} - \frac{1}{2PA} = \frac{3}{2PA}$$

hence $\quad PJ_a = \frac{2}{3} PA$

Because of the symmetry of the linkage, $PJ_b = PJ_a$. The pole tangent is horizontal (parallel to O_aO_b).

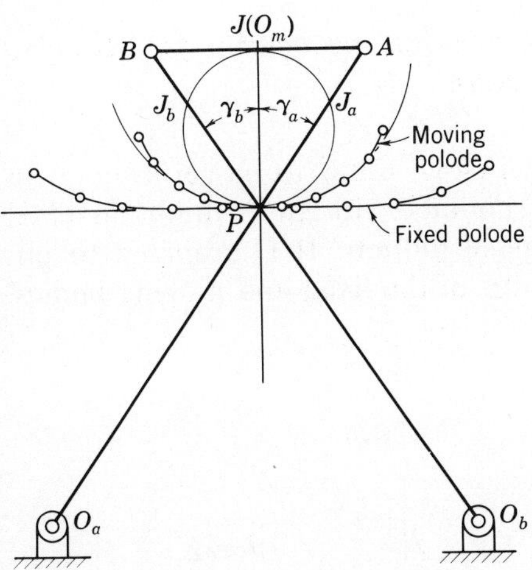

Fig. 6.3 Example in the use of the polode radius of curvature equation.

(2) The inflection circle diameter is

$$PJ = PJ_a/\cos\gamma_a = \tfrac{2}{3}(PA/\cos\gamma_a)$$

(3) The radius of the fixed polode is

$$R_f = O_fP = \frac{2PJ}{[3(PA/O_aA) - 1](1-K) + [3(PB/O_bB) - 1](1+K)}$$

where $K = \sin(\gamma_b + \gamma_a)/\sin(\gamma_b - \gamma_a)$. However, in this problem, $\gamma_b = -\gamma_a$; hence

$$K = O$$

So

$$R_f = \frac{\tfrac{2}{3}(PA/\cos\gamma_a)}{[(3)(\tfrac{1}{3}) - 1](1 - O) + [(3)(\tfrac{1}{3}) - 1](1 + O)} = \infty$$

The radius of the fixed polode is infinite and is independent of the angles γ_a, γ_b for this special case.

(4) The radius of the moving polode can now be found from the Euler-Savary equation.

$$\frac{1}{PO_m} = \frac{1}{PJ} + \frac{1}{PO_f} = \frac{1}{PJ} + \frac{1}{\infty} = \frac{1}{PJ}$$

The center of the moving polode is at J. The osculatory circle for the moving polode has twice the diameter of the inflection circle.

(5) Portions of the two polodes have been plotted in Fig. 6.3 as a check on the above results.

6.3 *Problem: designing a 4-bar mechanism for specified polode radii of curvature*

The cylinder shown in Fig. 6.4 is to be constrained to make approximate rolling contact with the cylindrical fixed surface, for a limited range of motion. It is proposed to pin joint two links between points of the fixed and moving bodies,

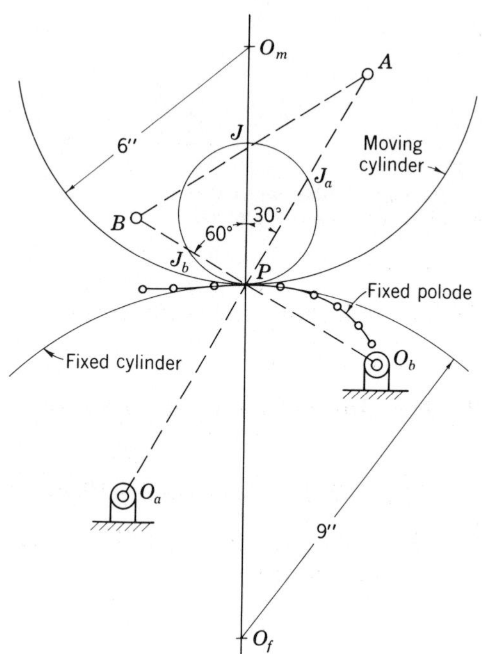

Fig. 6.4 Designing a 4-bar linkage to guide one cylinder in rolling contact with another.

thus forming a 4-bar mechanism with the moving cylinder as the coupler. We shall design it so that, in the design position, the centers of curvature of the polodes coincide with the centers of the fixed and moving cylinders.

(1) The inflection circle can be determined from the Euler-Savary equation.

$$\frac{1}{PJ}=\frac{1}{PO_m}-\frac{1}{PO_f}=\frac{1}{6}+\frac{1}{9}=\frac{15}{54}$$

$$PJ=3.60 \text{ in.}$$

(2) The polode curvature equation must be satisfied.

$$\frac{2(PJ)}{R_f}=\left[3\left(\frac{PA}{O_aA}\right)-1\right](1-K)$$
$$+\left[3\left(\frac{PB}{O_bB}\right)-1\right](1+K)$$

$$K=\frac{\sin(\gamma_b+\gamma_a)}{\sin(\gamma_b-\gamma_a)} \tag{1}$$

Also, the Euler-Savary equations must be satisfied.

$$O_aA=\frac{(PA)^2}{(PA-PJ\cos\gamma_a)} \tag{2}$$

$$O_bB=\frac{(PB)^2}{(PB-PJ\cos\gamma_b)} \tag{3}$$

Thus there are three equations to be satisfied, with six unknowns, PA, PB, O_aA, O_bB, γ_a, and γ_b.

(3) For a first solution to the problem we shall choose, arbitrarily,

$$\gamma_a=30 \text{ deg.} \qquad \gamma_b=-60 \text{ deg.} \qquad PA=2PJ_a$$

$$PA=2(3.60)\cos 30=6.23 \text{ in.}$$

$$K=\sin(-30)/\sin(-90)=0.50$$

$$O_aA=2PA$$

When all known quantities have been substituted in the polode curvature equation, the result is

$$PB=(0.456)O_bB$$

If this is solved simultaneously with Eq. (3), the result is

$$PB=3.31 \text{ in. and } O_bB=7.26 \text{ in.}$$

The resulting mechanism is shown with broken lines in Fig. 6.4. A portion of the fixed polode has been plotted for comparison with the fixed cylindrical surface. The agreement is not good. The fixed polode coincides with the fixed cylinder for an extremely short distance from the design position.

(4) A second, and better, solution to the problem is shown in Fig. 6.5. This is the 4-bar mechanism resulting from the following choices:

$$PA=PO_m \qquad \gamma_a=0 \text{ deg.} \qquad \gamma_b=30 \text{ deg.}$$

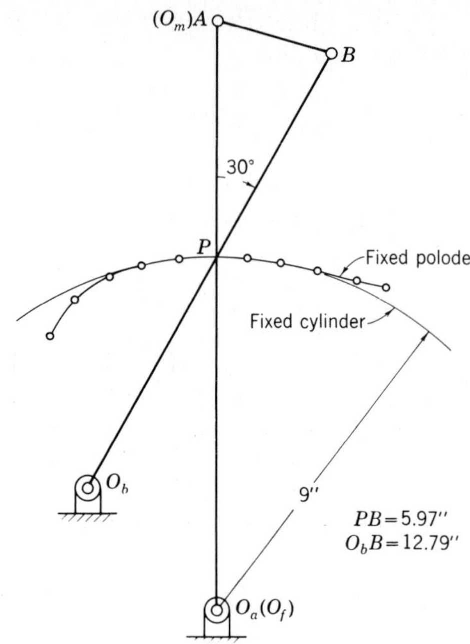

Fig. 6.5 Second solution to the design problem of Fig. 6.4.

(5) A third, and even better, solution is shown in Fig. 6.6. In this case the choices were

$$PA = PB \qquad \gamma_a = 30 \text{ deg.} \qquad \gamma_b = -30 \text{ deg.}$$

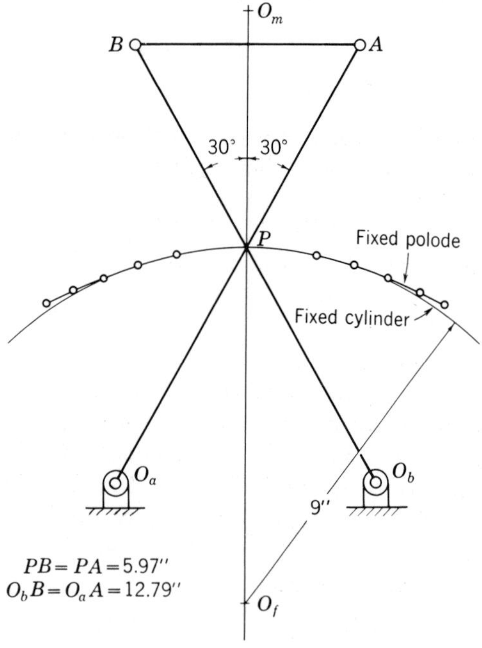

Fig. 6.6 Third solution to the design problem of Fig. 6.4.

6.4 *Polodes for the relative motion of the cranks in a 4-bar mechanism*

The polodes for the relative crank motion were discussed in Chapter 5. The results obtained there are listed again here. (See Fig. 6.7.)

$$R = nl/(n-1) \tag{1}$$

$$\frac{dR}{d\theta} = -\frac{(dn/d\theta)l}{(n-1)^2} \tag{2}$$

$$\tan\phi = -\frac{dn/d\theta}{n(n-1)} \tag{3}$$

where $n =$ angular velocity ratio, ω_4/ω_2

$R = O'P$

$\theta =$ rotation angle of crank 2 from the design position

$l = O'O$

$\phi =$ angle between the fixed link and the pole normal, or between a perpendicular to the fixed link and the pole tangent.

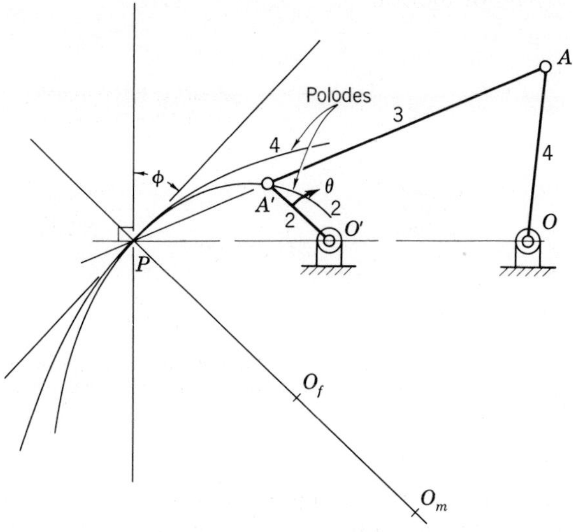

Fig. 6.7 Illustrating notation used in discussing polodes for relative motion of the cranks in a 4-bar mechanism.

Our objective now is to express the radius of curvature of one of the polodes in terms of the angular velocity ratio, n, and its derivatives with respect to θ. If we let R_f stand for the radius of curvature of the polode attached to link 2, the following expression holds:

$$R_f = \frac{[R^2 + (dR/d\theta)^2]^{3/2}}{R^2 + 2(dR/d\theta)^2 - R(d^2R/d\theta^2)} \tag{4}$$

If we differentiate Eq. (2) with respect to θ we have

$$\frac{d^2R}{d\theta^2} = \frac{l}{(n-1)^3}\left[2\left(\frac{dn}{d\theta}\right)^2 - (n-1)\left(\frac{d^2n}{d\theta^2}\right)\right] \tag{5}$$

After substitution of Eqs. (5), (2), and (1) in Eq. (4), the result is

$$R_f = \frac{l[n^2(n-1)^2 + (dn/d\theta)^2]^{3/2}}{[n^2(n-1) - 2(dn/d\theta)^2 + n(d^2n/d\theta^2)]\,(n-1)^3} \tag{6}$$

Rule for signs: The center of curvature O_f falls on the same side of the pole tangent as O' when the denominator on the right side of Eq. (6) is positive.

6.5 *Problem: designing a 4-bar mechanism to replace circular gears for a limited range of motion*

A 4-bar mechanism is required to replace a pair of circular gear segments. The gears have an angular velocity ratio of $-3{:}2$ and operate over a 30-deg. range of motion of the smaller gear. This velocity ratio must be held to within $\pm 1.0\%$ over the full range of motion.

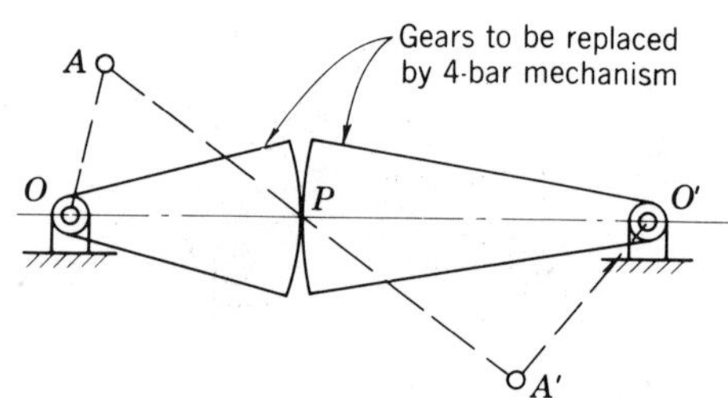

Fig. 6.8 Gears to be replaced by a 4-bar mechanism.

Since a rather narrow range of motion is involved and rather stringent specifications are placed on the angular velocity ratio, a procedure likely to yield good results is to design so that, in one position, (1) the velocity ratio, n, will be the desired value and (2) as many as possible of the derivatives of n, with respect to crank position, will be zero. Another way of expressing this is to say that we will design so that in the immediate vicinity of the design position the polodes of the relative motion will coincide as closely as possible with the gear pitch circles. In terms of symbols shown in Fig. 6.8, $n = O'P/OP$. We shall try to make $dn/d\theta = d^2n/d\theta^2 = 0$, which means so proportioning the 4-bar mechanism that the polodes for the relative crank motion will have centers of curvature at O and O'.

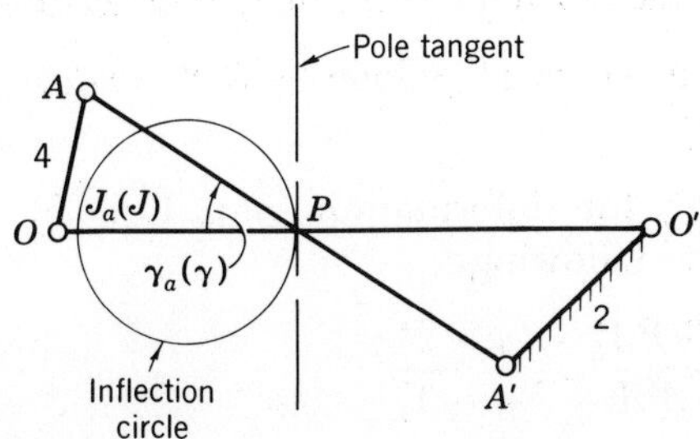

Fig. 6.9 Illustrating layout for design of a 4-bar to replace gears.

Refer to Fig. 6.9. Let $O'O = l$. For an angular velocity ratio, n, of crank OA to crank $O'A'$

$$O'P/OP = n \tag{1}$$

$$OP = l/(n-1) \tag{2}$$

$$O'P = nl/(n-1) \tag{3}$$

Now consider the motion of crank OA relative to crank $O'A'$. In this inverted motion point O is a moving point, and point O' is the center of curvature of its path. Hence the following Euler-Savary equation holds:

$$\frac{1}{PO} - \frac{1}{PO'} = \frac{1}{PJ_o} \tag{4}$$

The line $O'O$ is to be the pole normal, so point J_o is the inflection pole J. The diameter of the inflection circle along the pole normal is PJ. Substituting in Eq. (4) the values of PO and PO' from Eqs. (2) and (3) and writing PJ for PJ_o give

$$PJ = -nl/(n-1)^2 \tag{5}$$

The equation for radius of curvature of the polode associated with crank $O'A'$, the fixed link in the inverted motion under consideration, is

$$\frac{2(PJ)}{R} = \left[\frac{3(PA)}{A'A} - 1\right](1-K) + \left[\frac{3(PO)}{O'O} - 1\right](1+K) \tag{6}$$

where
$$K = \frac{\sin(\gamma_o + \gamma_a)}{\sin(\gamma_o - \gamma_a)} \tag{7}$$

In these equations

γ_o = angle from pole normal to line PO

= zero deg. in this problem

γ_a = angle from pole normal to PA line will be written γ.

R = radius of curvature of polode $= O'P = nl/(n-1)$ from Eq. (2).

Upon substituting this information, plus Eq. (5), we can reduce Eq. (6) to the following:

$$\frac{3(PA)}{A'A} = \frac{(n-2)}{(n-1)} \tag{8}$$

Since, in the inverted motion, A is a moving point with A' as the center of curvature of its path, the following Euler-Savary equation must be satisfied:

$$\frac{1}{PA} - \frac{1}{PA'} = \frac{1}{PJ_a} \tag{9}$$

but
$$PA' = PA - A'A$$

and
$$PJ_a = PJ\cos\gamma = -nl\cos\gamma/(n-1)^2$$

from Eq. (5)

Hence Eq. (9) becomes

$$PA(PA/A'A - 1) = nl\cos\gamma/(n-1)^2 \tag{10}$$

Elimination of $A'A$ between Eqs. (8) and (10) leaves

$$PA = \frac{3nl\cos\gamma}{(1-2n)(n-1)} \tag{11}$$

Substituting this in Eq. (10) yields

$$A'A = \frac{9nl\cos\gamma}{(2-n)(2n-1)} \tag{12}$$

Equations (11) and (12) define the locations of A and A' for any value of γ. The restrictions placed on the design were not enough to determine γ, so we are free to choose a value. For $\gamma = 30$ deg. the proportions of the mechanism will be as shown in Fig. 6.10(a).

Figure 6.10(b) shows the velocity ratio, n, as a function of displacement of crank OA from the design position. This curve was plotted from a layout in which the distance between crank pivots was made 15 in. In a layout of this size a change of 0.5% in the velocity ratio means a shift of less than 0.02 in. in the location of the point where the connecting rod crosses the line of pivots. Because of this the curve shown should not be relied upon to determine whether or not the mechanism designed meets the specifications. Points at the extremes of the range we intend to use should be checked by calculations. The calculated errors for $\beta = +13$ deg. and -17 deg. were found in this case to be 0.4% and 0.9%, respectively.

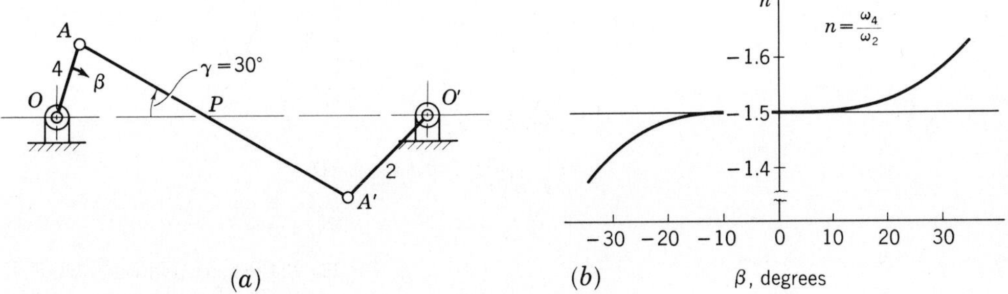

Fig. 6.10 (a) Mechanism designed. β is the angle of rotation of crank 4 from the design position. (b) Angular velocity ratio, n, versus β. The curve has inflection point with horizontal tangent at the design position, which is all that the design technique guarantees.

6.6 *Stationary curvature of point paths**

The path of a moving particle has "stationary curvature" at a given point if, at that point, the rate of change of path curvature with respect to distance along the path is zero. If we let ρ stand for radius of curvature and s stand for distance along the path, the condition for stationary curvature is that $d(1/\rho)/ds$ be zero.

For a rigid body in plane motion (the coupler of a 4-bar mechanism, for example), we are interested in discovering which particles at any given instant are located on points of stationary curvature of their paths. The question can be investigated by starting with the Euler-Savary equation for path curvature, differentiating, and setting the result equal to zero. It is more convenient to differentiate with respect to distance σ along the polode than to differentiate with respect to distance s along the path. This is permissible since $\dfrac{d(1/\rho)}{ds}$ must be zero whenever $\dfrac{d(1/\rho)}{d\sigma}$ is zero, except for the special case $d\sigma/ds = 0$.

* The treatment presented here is essentially that of Lorenzo Allievi in his book *Cinematica Della Biella Piana*, R. Tipographia Francesce Giannini & Figli, Napoli, 1895. This book is a collectors' item—apparently only a small number of copies were ever printed.

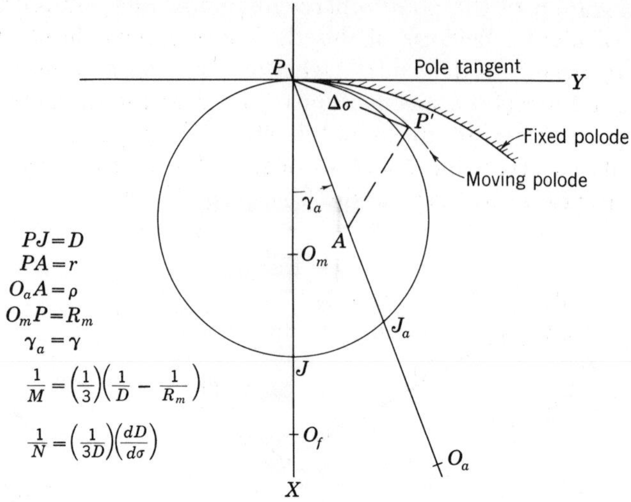

Fig. 6.11 Sketch and symbols used in discussion of stationary curvature.

The Euler-Savary equation (see Fig. 6.11) is

$$\rho = \frac{r^2}{(r - D\cos\gamma)} \tag{1}$$

After differentiating with respect to σ

$$-\rho^2 \frac{d(1/\rho)}{d\sigma} = \left(\frac{dr}{d\sigma}\right) \frac{2r}{r - D\cos\gamma} - \frac{r^2}{(r - D\cos\gamma)^2} \left[\left(\frac{dr}{d\sigma}\right) + D\sin\gamma\left(\frac{d\gamma}{d\sigma}\right) - \cos\gamma\left(\frac{dD}{d\sigma}\right)\right] \tag{2}$$

From Figs. 6.12 and 6.13, respectively,

$$dr/d\sigma = -\sin\gamma \tag{3}$$

$$\frac{d\gamma}{d\sigma} = -\frac{1}{R_m} - \frac{\cos\gamma}{r} \tag{4}$$

Substitution of (3) and (4) into (2), plus rearranging of terms, yields

$$\frac{d(1/\rho)}{d\sigma} = \frac{3D\sin\gamma\cos\gamma}{r^2}\left[\frac{1}{M\cos\gamma} - \frac{1}{N\sin\gamma} - \frac{1}{r}\right] \tag{5}$$

Our conclusion then is that, in general, a particle path will have stationary curvature if the particle is located on the curve defined by the equation

$$\frac{1}{r} = \frac{1}{M\cos\gamma} - \frac{1}{N\sin\gamma} \tag{6}$$

One name for this curve is "cubic of stationary curvature."

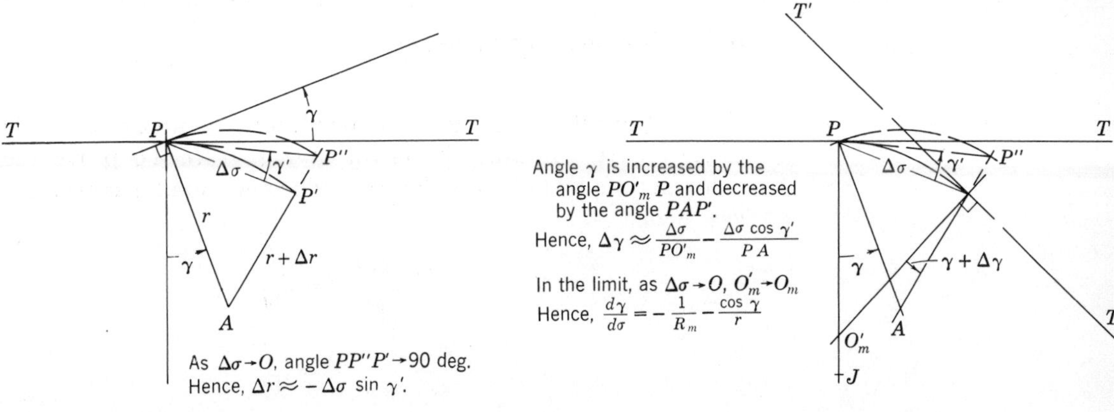

Fig. 6.12 Evaluation of $dr/d\sigma$.

Fig. 6.13 Evaluation of $d\gamma/d\sigma$.

That it is a cubic can be seen more clearly if the equation is converted to rectangular coordinates. It is suggested that the student do this. The general appearance of the curve is shown in Fig. 6.14. Listed below are some of its properties.

(a) Crosses the axes at P only. Tangent to both axes.

(b) Slope of asymptotes is M/N.

(c) Radius of curvature at $\gamma = 0$ or 180 deg. is $M/2$.

(d) Radius of curvature at $\gamma = 90$ or 270 deg. is $-N/2$.

(e) Maximum r (in the loop of the curve) is

$$MN/(M^{2/3} + N^{2/3})^{3/2}$$

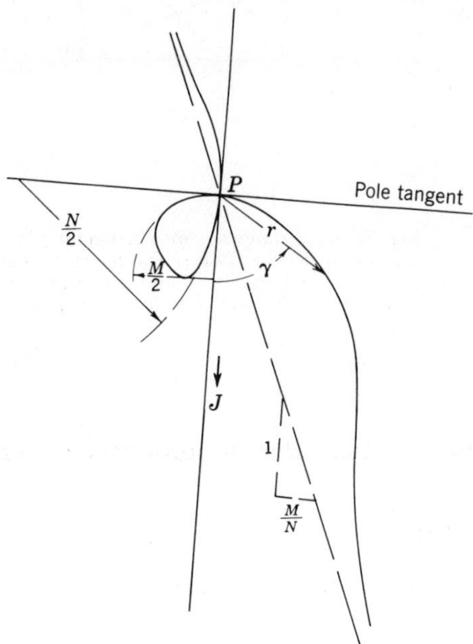

Fig. 6.14 Typical appearance of the cubic of stationary curvature.

6.7 Graphical construction

A graphical construction for plotting points on the cubic of stationary curvature is shown in Fig. 6.15. To prove the construction, first observe that triangle nPm is similar to triangle ngh, hence

$$\frac{(nP + Pg)}{gh} = \frac{N}{M}$$

or

$$\frac{(N + r/\sin\gamma)}{(r/\cos\gamma)} = \frac{N}{M}$$

Upon rearranging terms

$$\frac{1}{r} = \left(\frac{1}{M\cos\gamma}\right) - \left(\frac{1}{N\sin\gamma}\right)$$

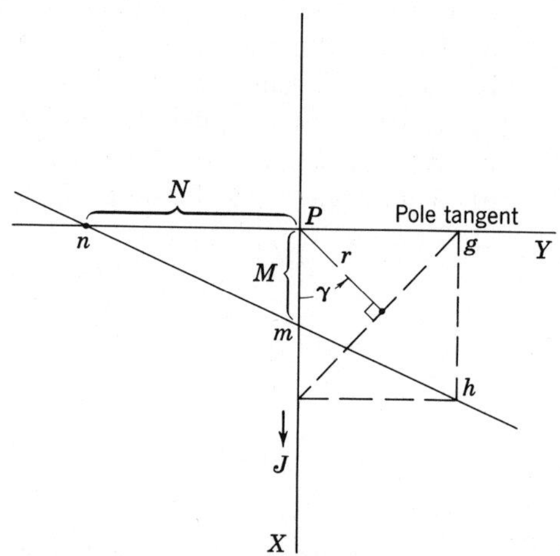

Fig. 6.15 A graphical construction for plotting points on the cubic of stationary curvature. To locate points m and n, measure M along the X axis and $-N$ along the Y axis.

6.8 Degenerate forms of the cubic of stationary curvature

The equation of the cubic may be written

$$\left(\frac{\sin\gamma\cos\gamma}{r}\right) - \left(\frac{\sin\gamma}{M}\right) + \left(\frac{\cos\gamma}{N}\right) = 0 \qquad (7)$$

For the special case $N = \infty$, the equation becomes

$$\sin\gamma\left(\frac{\cos\gamma}{r} - \frac{1}{M}\right) = 0 \tag{8}$$

This is the equation of a straight line (the pole normal), and a circle of diameter M tangent to the pole tangent at P.

For the special case $M = \infty$, the cubic equation becomes

$$\cos\gamma\left(\frac{\sin\gamma}{r} + \frac{1}{N}\right) = 0 \tag{9}$$

This is the equation of a straight line (the pole tangent) and a circle of diameter $-N$, tangent to the pole normal at P.

In the motion of the coupler of a 4-bar mechanism the case $N = \infty$ arises when one crankpin falls on the pole normal, as illustrated in Fig. 6.16. Degenerate forms of the cubic are also obtained under the following conditions:

(a) Both crankpins fall on a circle tangent to the pole tangent at the pole.
(b) Both crankpins fall on a circle tangent to the pole normal at the pole.
(c) One crankpin falls on the pole tangent.
(d) One crankpin falls on the pole normal and the other on the pole tangent.

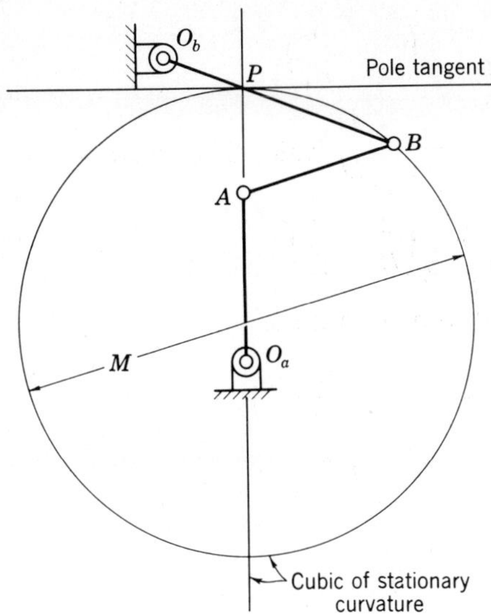

Fig. 6.16 A 4-bar mechanism in which one crankpin is located on the pole normal. The cubic of stationary curvature reduces to a straight line and circle.

6.9 Polode curvature

The following equation was previously derived from an acceleration analysis:

$$\frac{2(PJ)}{R_f} = \left[\frac{3PA}{O_aA} - 1\right](1 - K) + \left[\frac{3PB}{O_bB} - 1\right](1 + K)$$

$$K = \frac{\sin(\gamma_b + \gamma_a)}{\sin(\gamma_b - \gamma_a)} \tag{10}$$

This equation can also be derived from the cubic of stationary curvature. We start with the fact that the crankpins in a 4-bar mechanism must be located on the cubic of stationary curvature for motion of the coupler with respect to the fixed link.

$$\frac{1}{r_a} = \frac{1}{M\cos\gamma_a} - \frac{1}{N\sin\gamma_a} \tag{11}$$

$$\frac{1}{r_b} = \frac{1}{M\cos\gamma_b} - \frac{1}{N\sin\gamma_b} \tag{12}$$

From Eqs. (11) and (12) eliminate N.

$$\frac{\sin\gamma_a}{r_a} - \frac{\sin\gamma_b}{r_b} = \frac{1}{M}\left(\frac{\sin\gamma_a}{\cos\gamma_a} - \frac{\sin\gamma_b}{\cos\gamma_b}\right) \tag{13}$$

Express $1/M$ in terms of D and R_f.

$$\frac{1}{M} = \frac{1}{3}\left(\frac{1}{D} - \frac{1}{R_m}\right)$$

but

$$\frac{1}{R_m} = \frac{1}{R_f} - \frac{1}{D} \text{(Euler-Savary equation)}$$

hence

$$\frac{1}{M} = \frac{1}{3}\left(\frac{2}{D} - \frac{1}{R_f}\right) \tag{14}$$

Substitute (14) into (13) and rearrange.

$$\frac{D\cos\gamma_a}{r_a}\sin\gamma_a\cos\gamma_b - \left(\frac{D\cos\gamma_b}{r_b}\right)\sin\gamma_b\cos\gamma_a =$$

$$= \frac{1}{3}\left(2 - \frac{D}{R_f}\right)\sin(\gamma_a - \gamma_b) \tag{15}$$

Note that

$$\frac{D\cos\gamma_a}{r_a} = \frac{PJ_a}{PA} = 1 - \frac{PA}{O_aA}$$

$$\frac{D\cos\gamma_b}{r_b} = 1 - \frac{PB}{O_aB} \tag{16}$$

(Use the Euler-Savary equation to prove this.)
After the substitution of (16) into (15) and considerable rearrangement of terms, Eq. (10) will be obtained.

6.10 *Problem: cubic of stationary curvature for a circle rolling on a straight line*

Determine the cubic of stationary curvature for plane motion equivalent to the rolling of a circle along a fixed straight line. See Fig. 6.17.

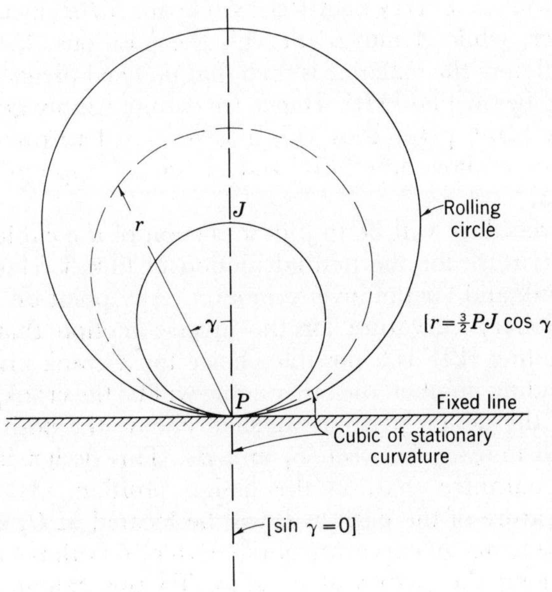

Fig. 6.17 Cubic of stationary curvature for a circle rolling on a straight line.

The circle is the moving polode, and the straight line the fixed polode. The diameter of the inflection circle is one-half the diameter of the rolling circle.

$$\frac{1}{M} = \frac{1}{3}\left(\frac{1}{D} - \frac{1}{R_m}\right)$$

but $$D = PJ \quad \text{and} \quad R_m = -PJ$$

hence $$\frac{1}{M} = \tfrac{2}{3}(PJ)$$

The diameter of the inflection circle does not change with the motion, hence

$$\frac{1}{N} = \frac{1}{3D}\frac{dD}{d\sigma} = 0$$

Therefore the cubic has the degenerate form consisting of the circle, $r = 3/2\,PJ\cos\gamma$, and the straight line, $\sin\gamma = 0$.

6.11 *Problem: design based on the cubic of stationary curvature*

Fig. 6.18 shows a slider, link 2, moving horizontally and, pin-jointed to it, another link, 3, which is required to move so that point B will travel very nearly the circle arc B_1BB_2 around O_b as a center, while A moves through the positions A_1AA_2. The construction of the machine is such that no fixed pivots can be established below line WW. Hence we cannot simply guide point B by a crank pivoted at O_b. It is proposed to pivot a crank somewhere above line WW and pin to an appropriate point of link 3.

Our procedure will be to plot a portion of the cubic of stationary curvature for the desired motion of link 3 relative to the fixed link and for the inverse motion. Any point on the cubic of stationary curvature for the inverse motion that is located above line WW is a possible choice for a crank pivot. The corresponding point on the other cubic will be the crankpin location. For the design position we shall choose the position shown, with B midway between B_1 and B_2. This design procedure will guarantee that, in the design position, (1) the center of curvature of the path of B will be located at O_b and (2) the rate of change of curvature of the path of B with respect to distance along the path will be zero. To this extent the actual path of B will approximate the desired circle arc. How closely B follows the circle arc away from the design position we can determine by plotting the actual path after a tentative design is found.

(1) Determine the pole tangent, pole normal, and inflection circle for the motion of link 3 relative to the fixed link.

(2) Measure the angles γ_a, γ_b and the distances $PA = r_a$, $PB = r_b$. Then determine the constants M and N in the equation for the cubic of stationary curvature by solving the following simultaneously:

$$\frac{1}{r_a} = \frac{1}{M\cos\gamma_a} - \frac{1}{N\sin\gamma_a}$$

$$\frac{1}{r_b} = \frac{1}{M\cos\gamma_b} - \frac{1}{N\sin\gamma_b}$$

(3) Having established M and N, plot a portion of the cubic in the vicinity of point B.

(4) Plot corresponding points on the cubic for the inverse motion (link 1 relative to link 3). Any point C on the cubic for motion of 3 relative to 1 is related to the corresponding point O_c on the cubic for motion of 1 relative to 3 through the Euler-Savary equation

$$\frac{1}{PC} - \frac{1}{PO_c} = \frac{1}{PJ_c}$$

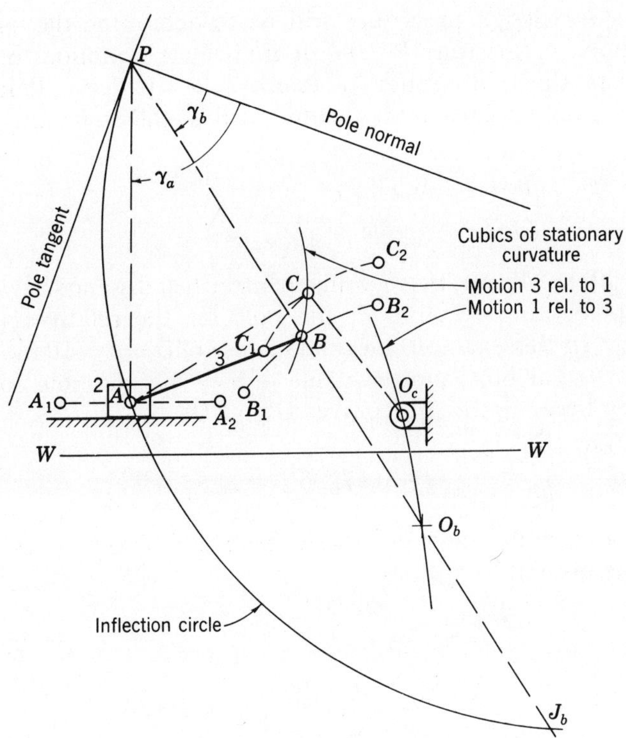

Fig. 6.18 Design based on the cubic of stationary curvature.

(5) Choose a point O_c above line WW for the pivot of the crank, and establish the crankpin at C.

(6) Plot the actual path of B as determined by the mechanism designed. If agreement with the circle arc is not satisfactory, try other locations for O_c and C.

6.12 *Problem: design of a 4-bar mechanism for coordinated crank positions*

A 4-bar mechanism is required such that the angular displacements of the cranks will obey the following relation:

$$\beta = -0.286480^2 - \theta$$

where θ is the displacement of the input crank (to be called link 2) from the design position and β is the displacement of the output crank (link 4), both in radians. Exact agreement with this equation is not expected. An error of ± 0.2 deg. in β is acceptable within the range of θ between -20 and $+20$ deg. The mechanism is not to be used outside this range.

Our design procedure will be to determine the cubics of stationary curvature for the desired relative motions of the cranks in the mid-position of crank 2 ($\theta = 0$ deg.). Pairs of corresponding points on these cubics will be the crank pins and pivots.

(1) $d\beta/d\theta = -0.57296\,\theta - 1$

$$\text{at } \theta = 0, \quad d\beta/d\theta = \omega_4/\omega_2 = n = -1$$

Start a layout by choosing arbitrarily a distance between fixed pivots and locating P, the pole for the relative crank motion. In this example we shall choose $O'O = l = 10$ in. See Fig. 6.19. For our required value of $n = -1$, the pole comes midway between the fixed pivots O and O'.

(2) $\dfrac{dn}{d\theta} = \dfrac{d^2\beta}{d\theta^2} = -0.57296$

Determine angle ϕ between the fixed link (line $O'O$) and the pole normal.

$$\tan\phi = -\frac{(dn/d\theta)}{n(n-1)}$$

$$= -\frac{(-0.57296)}{-1(-1-1)} = 0.28648$$

$$\phi = 15.99 \text{ deg.}$$

Add the pole tangent and pole normal to the layout.

(3) For motion of crank 4 relative to 2, the inflection circle crosses the PO line at J_o, where

$$\frac{1}{PJ_o} = \frac{1}{PO} - \frac{1}{PO'}$$

$$= 1/5 - 1/-5 = -2/5$$

$$PJ_o = 2.500 \text{ in.}$$

The diameter of the inflection circle is

$$PJ = \frac{PJ_o}{\cos \phi}$$

$$= \frac{2.500}{\cos 15.99} = 2.601 \text{ in.}$$

(4) The radius of curvature of the polode attached to crank 2 is to be

$$R_f = l \frac{[n^2(n-1)^2 + (dn/d\theta)^2]^{3/2}}{[n^2(n-1) - 2(dn/d\theta)^2 + n(d^2n/d\theta^2)](n-1)^3}$$

$$= 10 \frac{[(1)(4) + (-0.57296)^2]^{3/2}}{[-2 - 2(-0.57296)^2 - (0)](-8)}$$

$$= 4.237 \text{ in.}$$

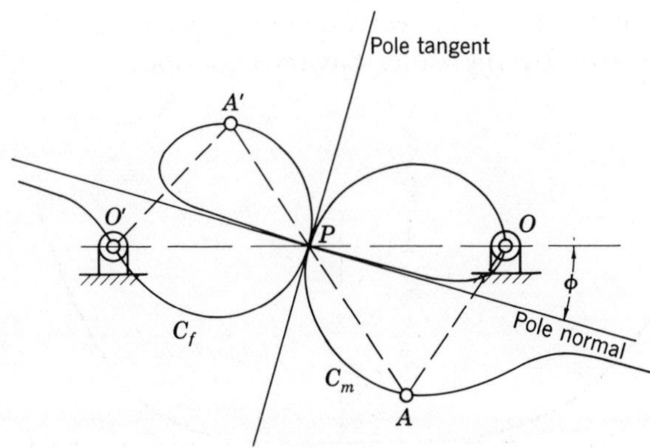

Fig. 6.19 Layout for design of a 4-bar mechanism for coordinated crank motions. Cubics of stationary curvature C_m (moving) and C_f (fixed).

Since the denominator in the expression above is positive, O_f falls on the same side of the pole tangent as O'.

(5) The radius of curvature of the moving polode (for motion of crank 4 relative to 2) can now be determined from the Euler-Savary equation

$$\frac{1}{PO_m} = \frac{1}{PO_f} + \frac{1}{PJ} = -\frac{1}{4.237} + \frac{1}{2.601} = +0.1485$$

$$O_mP = 6.735 \text{ in.}$$

(6) The constant M in the equation for the cubic of stationary curvature for motion of 4 relative to 2 can now be determined.

$$1/M = (1/3)(1/PJ - 1/O_mP)$$
$$= (1/3)(1/2.601 + 1/6.735) = 0.1777$$
$$M = 5.628.$$

(7) Point O belongs to the cubic of stationary curvature. Hence

$$1/PO = 1/(M\cos\gamma_0) - 1/(N\sin\gamma_0)$$
$$1/5 = 1/(5.628\cos 15.99) - 1/(N\sin 15.99)$$

from which $N = 239.3$

The equation of the cubic of stationary curvature is therefore

$$1/r = 1/(5.628\cos\gamma) - 1/(239.3\sin\gamma)$$

This is curve C_m plotted in Fig. 6.19.

(8) The cubic of stationary curvature, C_f, for the inverse motion (2 relative to 4) can be plotted either by first evaluating the constants M and N in the equation for this motion or by making use of the fact that corresponding points on the two cubics are related by the Euler-Savary equation.

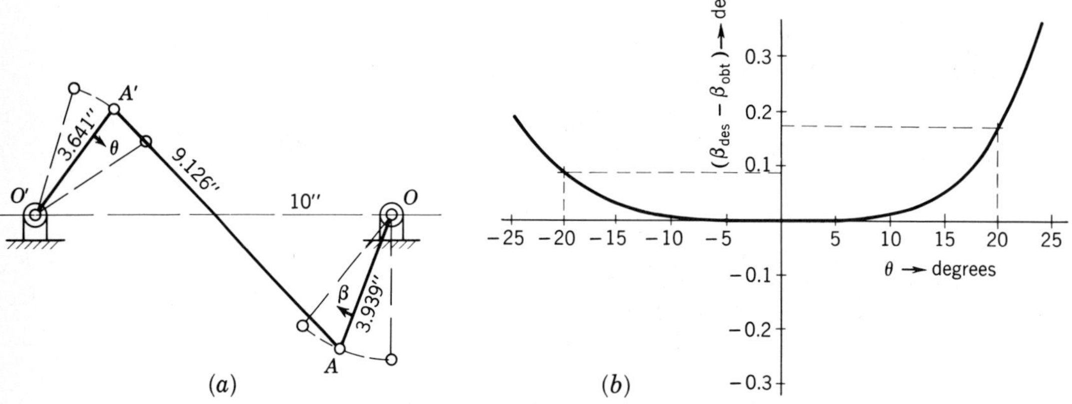

Fig. 6.20 (a) One mechanism obtained from the layout in Fig. 6.19. (b) Error curve for the above mechanism. Difference between angle β desired and that actually obtained, versus θ.

(9) Possible solutions to our design problem are obtained by making a pair of corresponding points on the two cubics the crankpins A and A'. One resulting mechanism is shown in Fig. 6.20, along with a curve showing the error in the function generated.

Problems and Exercises

E6.1 Draw a 4-bar mechanism of approximately the proportions shown in Fig. 6.1. Assume an angular velocity (constant) for crank 2 and make an acceleration analysis to determine the pole acceleration. Use the scaled values from your velocity and acceleration diagrams to determine the radius of curvature of the fixed polode from the equation $R_f = u^2/A_p^n$. Check this value for R_f by use of the polode curvature equation developed in Art. 6.1.

E6.2 In the mechanism of Fig. 6.21 locate the center of curvature of the fixed polode for motion of 3 relative to 1.

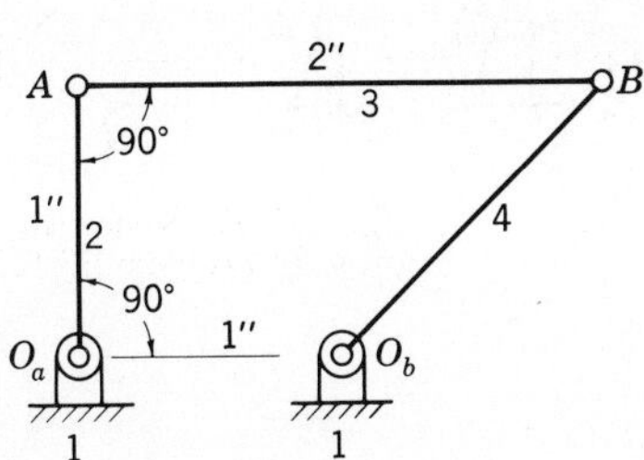

Fig. 6.21 Mechanism for problem E6.2.

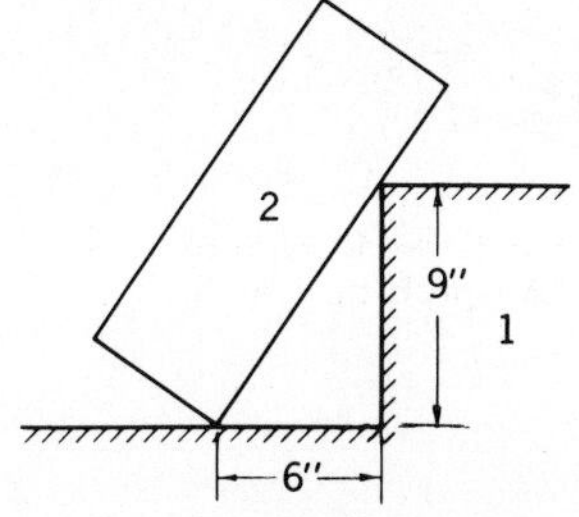

Fig. 6.22 Diagram for problem E6.3.

E6.3 Refer to Fig. 6.22. For motion of 2 relative to 1, in the position shown, locate the centers of curvature of the fixed and moving polodes.

E6.4 Design a 4-bar mechanism such that in the design position the radii of curvature of both polodes for the motion of the connecting rod relative to the fixed link shall be 5 in. The centers of curvature of the polodes are to lie on opposite sides of the pole tangent.

E6.5 A rule for signs is stated at the end of Art. 6.4, under Eq. (6). Prove this rule.

E6.6 Refer to Fig. 6.23. Link 2, pivoted at O_2, is to make rolling contact over its flat face with link 3, pivoted at O_3. The angular velocity of 2 is 1 rad. ps, constant. For the position shown, determine the angular velocity, angular acceleration, and rate of change of angular acceleration for link 3.

E6.7 Design a 4-bar mechanism such that, in the design position, the angular velocity ratio of the cranks shall be $n = 3$ and $dn/d\theta = d^2n/d\theta^2 = 0$.

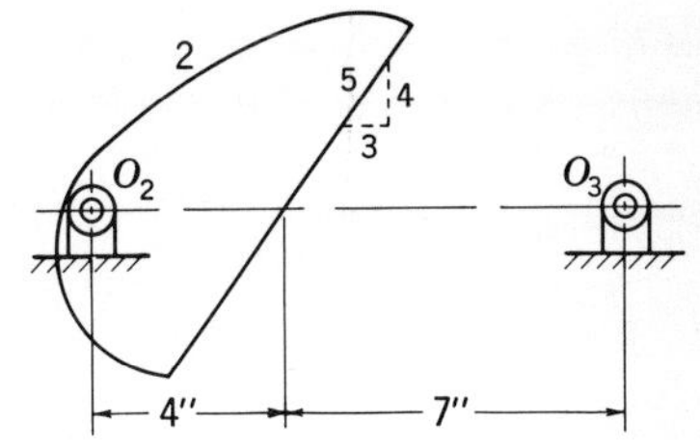

Fig. 6.23 Diagram for problem E6.6.

E6.8 Refer to Fig. 6.24. Determine the location of those points, belonging to link 3, whose paths have stationary curvature of 12 in. radius in the given position of the mechanism.

E6.9 What form is taken by the cubic of stationary curvature for motion of the coupler relative to the fixed link in a 4-bar mechanism when one crank lies along the pole normal and the other along the pole tangent?

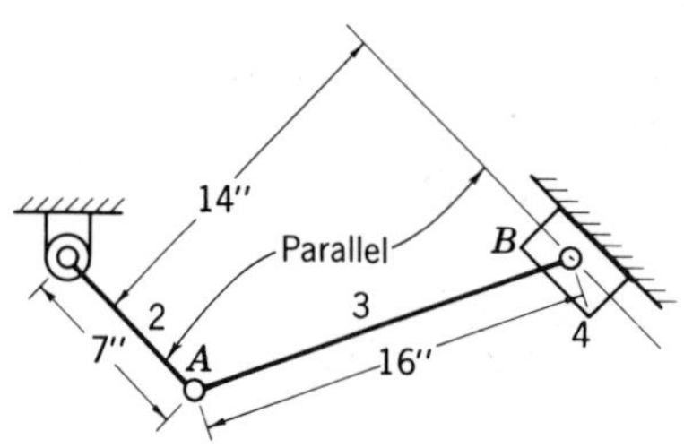

Fig. 6.24 Mechanism for problem E6.8.

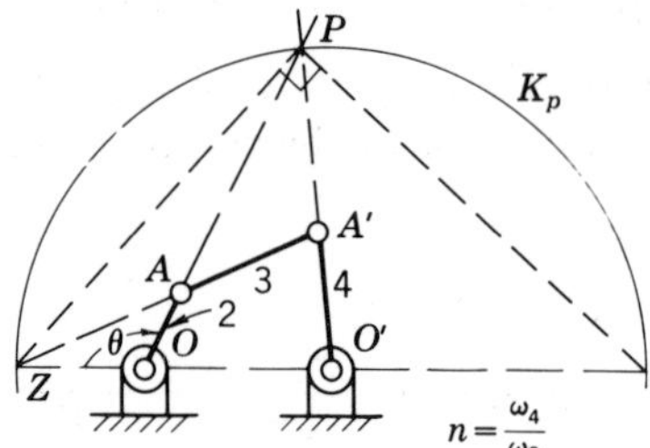

Fig. 6.25 Reference diagram for problem E6.12.

E6.10 Determine the cubic of stationary curvature for the rolling of a straight line on a circle. Compare the result with Art. 6.10.

E6.11 Design a 4-bar mechanism such that, in the design position, the angular velocity ratio of the cranks shall be $\omega_2/\omega_4 = n = 0$, $dn/d\theta = -10$ rad^{-1}, and $d^2n/d\theta^2 = 0$.

E6.12 Refer to Fig. 6.25. A family of 4-bar mechanisms is defined by specified values of n, $dn/d\theta$, and $d^2n/d\theta^2$. Prove that, for all members of this family drawn with pivots O and O', circle K_p contains pole P.

7

Analytical design of 4-bar mechanism for coordinated motions of the cranks

7.1 *Freudenstein's equation*

A relation between crank angles and link lengths in the 4-bar mechanism can be developed by considering the links as vectors. (See Fig. 7.1). The sum of the X components must be zero.

$$b \cos \beta - c \cos \phi + d + a \cos \theta = 0 \tag{1}$$

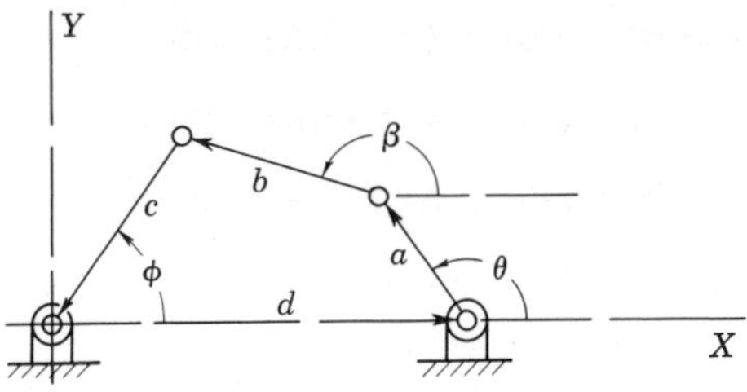

Fig. 7.1 Reference sketch for development of Freudenstein's 4-bar equation.

The sum of the Y components must be zero.

$$b \sin \beta - c \sin \phi + a \sin \theta = 0 \tag{2}$$

Rearranging, and squaring both sides of Eqs. (1) and (2), yields

$$b^2 \cos^2 \beta = (c \cos \phi - d - a \cos \theta)^2 \tag{3}$$

$$b^2 \sin^2 \beta = (c \sin \phi - a \sin \theta)^2 \tag{4}$$

Expanding the right-hand sides of these equations, then adding, yields

$$b^2 = c^2 + d^2 + a^2 - 2dc \cos \phi - 2ca \cos \phi \cos \theta - 2ca \sin \phi \sin \theta - 2da \cos \theta \tag{5}$$

which may be rewritten

$$\begin{aligned} R_1 \cos \theta - R_2 \cos \phi + R_3 &= \cos (\theta - \phi) \\ R_1 &= d/c \\ R_2 &= d/a \\ R_3 &= \frac{(d^2 + a^2 - b^2 + c^2)}{2ca} \end{aligned} \tag{6}$$

This is the Freudenstein (6) equation for the 4-bar mechanism, probably the most useful form for design problems requiring coordinated motions of the two cranks.

7.2 *Sample design problem, three coordinated crank positions*

A 4-bar mechanism is required such that the crank angles will be coordinated as follows:

θ, deg...	0	30	60
ϕ, deg...	30	50	80

(1) Write the Freudenstein equation for each of the three mechanism positions required.

$$R_1 \cos 0 - R_2 \cos 30 + R_3 = \cos (-30)$$

$$R_1 \cos 30 - R_2 \cos 50 + R_3 = \cos (-20)$$

$$R_1 \cos 60 - R_2 \cos 80 + R_3 = \cos (-20)$$

(2) Solve this set of equations for R_1, R_2, and R_3.

$$R_1 = 1.8321$$

$$R_2 = 1.4294$$

$$R_3 = 0.2718$$

(3) Choose one link length and solve for the others from the expressions for R_1, R_2, and R_3 of Eq. (6). In this example we chose $a = 1.000$ and calculated $d = 1.429$, $b = 1.797$, and $c = 0.780$ units. The resulting mechanism is shown in Fig. 7.2.

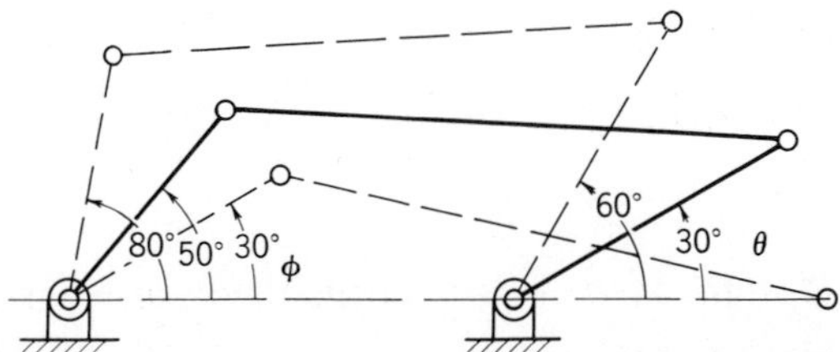

Fig. 7.2 Mechanism designed for three coordinated pairs of crank positions, using Freudenstein's equation.

7.3 *Coordination of crank velocities and derivatives*

Freudenstein's equation is

$$R_1 \cos\theta - R_2 \cos\phi + R_3 = \cos(\theta - \phi) \tag{7}$$

Successive differentiation with respect to θ yields

$$R_1 \begin{Bmatrix} \sin\theta \\ \cos\theta \end{Bmatrix} + R_2(a_i \sin\phi + b_i \cos\phi) = c_i \sin(\theta - \phi) + d_i \cos(\theta - \phi) \tag{8}$$

where $i = 1, 2, 3$, etc., for first, second, third differentiations. The first term of Eq. (8) is $R_1 \sin\theta$ for odd i's and $R_1 \cos\theta$ for even i's. Values of a_i, b_i, c_i, and d_i are listed below for $i = 1, 2, 3$, and 4.

i	a_i	b_i	c_i	d_i
1	$-n_1$	0	$1 - n_1$	0
2	$-n_2$	$-n_1^2$	$-n_2$	$(1 - n_1)^2$
3	$-n_1^3 + n_3$	$3n_1n_2$	$(1 - n_1)^3 + n_3$	$3(1 - n_1)(n_2)$
4	$n^4 - 6n_1^2n_2$	$4n_1n_3 - n_1^4 + 3n_2^2$	$n_4 - 6n_2(1 - n_1)^2$	$4n_3(1 - n_1) + (1 - n_1)^4 - 3n_2^2$

$$n_i = d^i\phi/d\theta^i \qquad (n_1 = d\phi/d\theta,\ n_2 = d^2\phi/d\theta^2, \text{ etc.})$$

For a fourth-order approximation to a desired functional relation between θ and ϕ, Eqs. (7) and (8) must be solved for $i = 1, 2$, and 3. If we eliminate R_1 and R_2 from Eq. (8) for $i = 1, 2$, and 3, the result is

$$\lambda_1 \tan^2\theta + \lambda_2 \tan\theta + \lambda_3 = 0 \tag{9}$$

where

$$\lambda_1 = D_2(E_3 - E_1) - E_2(D_3 - D_1) \quad (10)$$

$$\lambda_2 = E_2(F_1 - F_3) - D_1E_3 + E_1D_3 + F_2(E_3 - E_1) \quad (11)$$

$$\lambda_3 = E_1(F_3 - F_1) - F_1(E_3 - E_1) \quad (12)$$

$$E_i = a_i \sin\phi + b_i \cos\phi \quad (13)$$

$$D_i = c_i \cos\phi + d_i \sin\phi \quad (14)$$

$$F_i = d_i \cos\phi - c_i \sin\phi \quad (15)$$

7.4 *Problem: design of a 4-bar mechanism for constant angular-velocity ratio of the cranks*

A 4-bar mechanism is required such that the crank angular-velocity ratio shall be very nearly -1 for a 40-deg. range of motion of one crank.

We shall attempt to find a suitable design by using the results of the previous article, designing so that $n_1 = -1$, $n_2 = 0$, and $n_3 = 0$, in the design position.

PROCEDURE

(1) Calculate the coefficients a_i, b_i, c_i and d_i.

i	a_i	b_i	c_i	d_i
1	1	0	2	0
2	0	−1	0	4
3	1	0	8	0

(2) Make a tentative choice of angle ϕ and calculate E_i, D_i, and F_i. For angle $\phi = 45$ deg.

$$E_1 = (1)(0.707) + 0 = 0.707$$

$$E_2 = 0 - (1)(0.707) = -0.707$$

$$E_3 = (1)(0.707) + 0 = 0.707$$

$$D_1 = 2(0.707) + 0 = 1.414$$

$$D_2 = 0 + 4(0.707) = 2.828$$

$$D_3 = 8(0.707) + 0 = 5.656$$

$$F_1 = 0 - 2(0.707) = -1.414$$

$$F_2 = 4(0.707) - 0 = 2.828$$

$$F_3 = 0 - 8(0.707) = -5.656$$

(3) Calculate λ_i

$$\lambda_1 = 2.828(0.707 - 0.707) + 0.707(5.656 - 1.414) = 3.00$$

$$\lambda_2 = -0.707(5.656 - 1.414) - 1.414(0.707 + 0.707(5.656) + 2.826(0.707 - 0.707) = 0$$

$$\lambda_3 = +0.707(-5.656 + 1.414) + 1.414(0.707 - 0.707) = -3.000$$

(4) Equation (9) of the previous article is then

$$3\tan^2\theta - 3 = 0$$

or

$$\tan^2\theta - 1 = 0$$

hence

$$\tan\theta = \pm 1$$

$$\theta = \pm 45^0$$

(5) Taking $\theta = +45^0$, we now write Eqs. (7) and (8) of the previous article.

$$R_1\cos(+45^0) - R_2\cos 45^0 + R_3 = \cos(0^0)$$

$$R_1\sin(+45^0) + R_2(0.707) = 2\sin(0^0) + 0\cos(0^0)$$

$$R_1\cos(+45^0) + R_2(-0.707) = 0\sin(0^0) + 4\cos(-0^0)$$

$$R_1\sin(+45^0) + R_2(0.707) = 8\sin(0^0) + 0\cos(-0^0)$$

or

$$0.707\,R_1 - 0.707\,R_2 + R_3 = 1$$

$$+0.707\,R_1 + 0.707\,R_2 = 0$$

$$0.707\,R_1 - 0.707\,R_2 = 4$$

$$+0.707\,R_1 + 0.707\,R_2 = 0$$

hence

$$R_1 = 1.414$$

$$R_2 = -1.414$$

$$R_3 = -3.000$$

(6) Link lengths are, for $d = 10$ in.

$$c = \frac{d}{R_1} = \frac{10}{1.414} = 5(0.707) = 3.535 \text{ in.}$$

$$a = \frac{d}{R_2} = \frac{-10}{1.414} = -3.535 \text{ in.}$$

$$R_3 = \frac{d^2 + a^2 - b^2 + c^2}{2ca}$$

$$-3.000 = \frac{10^2 + 3.535^2 + 3.535_2 - b^2}{2(3.535)(-3.535)}$$

$$-3.000 = \frac{100 + 12.5 + 12.5 - b^2}{-25}$$

$$75 = 125 - b^2$$

$$b^2 = 50$$

$$b = \sqrt{50} = 7.07 \text{ in.}$$

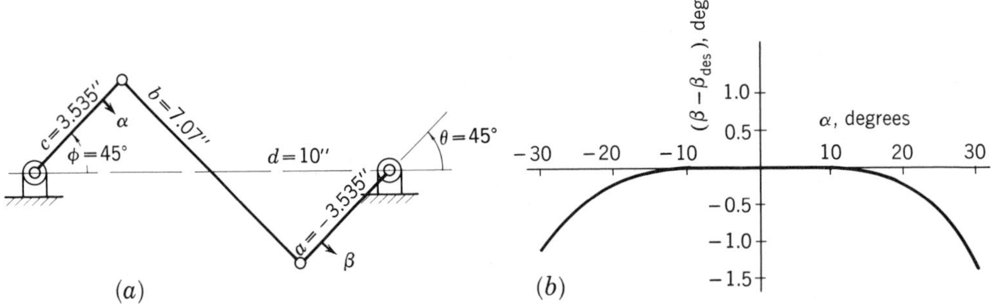

Fig. 7.3 (a) A 4-bar mechanism designed for nearly constant angular velocity ratio = −1. (b) Error curve for the above mechanism.

The mechanism we have arrived at is shown in Fig. 7.3(a). Fig. 7.3(b) shows the error in output displacement for a range of approximately 30 deg. each way from the design position. Within the 40-deg. range of motion mentioned in the specifications, the maximum error in position of the output crank is less than $\frac{1}{4}$ deg.

7.5 *Alternate form of results for fourth-order approximation*

If designs are to be found for a series of values of ϕ, the following form for Eq. (9) will be more convenient:

$$\lambda_1' \tan^2\theta + \lambda_2' \tan\theta + \lambda_3' = 0 \tag{16}$$

where $$\lambda_k' = l_k + p_k \tan\phi + q_k \tan^2\phi \tag{17}$$

$$l_1 = c_2(b_3 - b_1) - b_2(c_3 - c_1) \tag{18}$$

$$l_2 = d_2(b_3 - b_1) - b_2(d_3 - d_1) + b_1c_3 - b_3c_1 \tag{19}$$

$$l_3 = b_1(d_3 - d_1) - d_1(b_3 - b_1) \tag{20}$$

$$p_1 = c_2(a_3 - a_1) - a_2(c_3 - c_1) + d_2(b_3 - b_1) - b_2(d_3 - d_1) \qquad (21)$$

$$p_2 = d_2(a_3 - a_1) - a_2(d_3 - d_1) + b_2(c_3 - c_1) - c_2(b_3 - b_1) + a_1c_3 - a_3c_1 + b_1d_3 - b_3d_1 \qquad (22)$$

$$p_3 = a_1(d_3 - d_1) - d_1(a_3 - a_1) + c_1(b_3 - b_1) - b_1(c_3 - c_1) \qquad (23)$$

$$q_1 = d_2(a_3 - a_1) - a_2(d_3 - d_1) \qquad (24)$$

$$q_2 = a_2(c_3 - c_1) - c_2(a_3 - a_1) + a_1d_3 - a_3d_1 \qquad (25)$$

$$q_3 = c_1(a_3 - a_1) - a_1(c_3 - c_1) \qquad (26)$$

Note: Division by $\cos^2 \phi$ was involved in deriving Eq. (16); Hence, for $\phi = 90$ or 270 deg. Eq. (17) is not valid. For this special case

$$\lambda'_k = q_k$$

Substitution of the expressions for a_i, b_i, c_i, and d_i in terms of n_i into Eqs. (18)–(26) will show that l_2, l_3, p_1, p_3, and q_2 are zero. Hence Eq. (16) reduces to the form

$$(f + g\tan^2\phi)\tan^2\theta + (h\tan\phi)\tan\theta + k\tan^2\phi = 0 \qquad (27)$$

where

$$f = c_2b_3 - c_3b_2 - c_1b_2 \qquad (28)$$

$$g = d_2a_3 - d_3a_2 - d_2a_1 \qquad (29)$$

$$k = c_1a_3 - c_3a_1 \qquad (30)$$

$$h = g - f - k \qquad (31)$$

7.6 *Problem: fourth-order design of 4-bar mechanism to generate log function*

A 4-bar mechanism is to be designed to generate the function

$$y = \ln x$$

with high precision in the vicinity of $x = 5.5$. Scales are to be such that the crank associated with x would rotate 90 deg. for $1 < x < 10$ and the corresponding rotation of the output crank would be 60 deg.

(1) $$K_x = \frac{\Delta x}{\Delta\theta} = \frac{(10 - 1)}{\pi/2} = 5.729577\,\frac{\text{units}}{\text{rad.}}$$

$$K_y = \frac{\Delta y}{\Delta\theta} = \frac{(\ln 10 - \ln 1)}{\pi/3} = \pm 2.198811\,\frac{\text{units}}{\text{rad.}}$$

K_y is $\pm$ depending upon whether we design for the two cranks to rotate in the same or opposite directnois.

(2) $$n_1 = \frac{d\phi}{d\theta} = \frac{K_x}{K_y}\frac{dy}{dx} = \frac{K_x}{K_y}(x^{-1})$$

$$n_2 = \frac{d^2\phi}{d\theta^2} = \frac{K_x^2}{K_y}\frac{d^2y}{dx^2} = \frac{K_x^2}{K_y}(-x^{-2})$$

$$n_3 = \frac{d^3\phi}{d\theta^3} = \frac{K_x^3}{K_y}\frac{d^3y}{dx^3} = \frac{K_x^3}{K_y}(2x^{-3})$$

(3) At $x = 5.5$, for K_y positive

$n_1 = 0.473775$

$n_2 = -0.493551$

$n_3 = 1.028304$

(4) Calculate and tabulate a_i, b_i, c_i, and d_i.

i	a_i	b_i	c_i	d_i
1	−0.473775	0	0.526225	0
2	0.493551	−0.224463	0.493551	0.276913
3	0.921959	−0.701496	1.174023	−0.779157

(5) Calculate f, g, k, and h.

$f = -0.200817$

$g = 0.771051$

$h = -0.069513$

$k = 1.041380$

(6) Select a trial value for ϕ and calculate the coefficients in Eq. (27). For $\phi = -25$ deg.:

$f + g\tan^2\phi = -0.033157$

$h\tan\phi = 0.032414$

$k\tan^2\phi = 0.226441$

(7) Eq. (27) is then

$$-0.033157\tan^2\theta + 0.032414\tan\theta + 0.226441 = 0$$

or $$\tan^2\theta - 0.9776\tan\theta - 6.8285 = 0$$

from which $$\tan\theta = 3.1473 \text{ or } -2.1697$$

$$\theta = 72.37 \text{ or } -65.26 \text{ deg.}$$

(8) Substituting $\phi = -25$ deg. and $\theta = 72.37$ deg. into Eqs. (7) and (8) and solving, we obtain

$$R_1 = 0.6746$$

$$R_2 = -0.6059$$

$$R_3 = -0.8818$$

(9) If we choose $d = 10$ in., then

$$a = -16.50 \text{ in.}$$

$$b = 12.68 \text{ in.}$$

$$c = 14.82 \text{ in.}$$

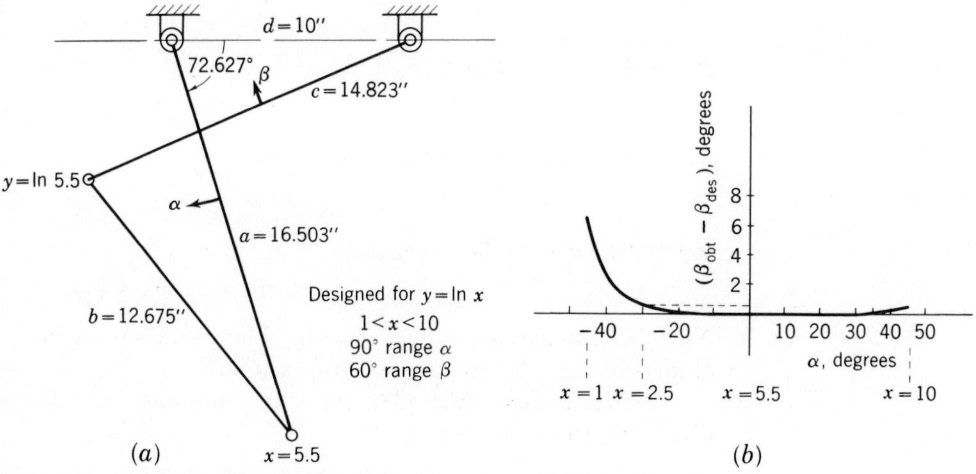

Fig. 7.4 (a) Mechanism designed to generate the function $y = \ln x$ with maximum accuracy in the vicinity of $x = 5.5$. (b) Error curve for the above mechanism.

(10) The mechanism designed is shown in Fig. 7.4, along with the error curve. For -30 deg. $< \alpha < 45$ deg. (corresponding to $2.5 < x < 10$) the design is quite good, but the error rapidly increases outside this range. Better accuracy in the lower part of the x range could be obtained by designing at a lower x value. Designing at $x = 4.3$ should produce a more nearly symmetrical error curve for the range $1 < x < 10$.

7.7 *4-point approximation, coordinated crank displacements*

To design a 4-bar mechanism to generate a desired function with four precision points, we might write the Freudenstein equation for four values of θ and ϕ.

$$R_1 \cos \theta_0 - R_2 \cos \phi_0 + R_3 = \cos (\theta_0 - \phi_0) \tag{32}$$

$$R_1 \cos \theta_1 - R_2 \cos \phi_1 + R_3 = \cos (\theta_1 - \phi_1) \tag{33}$$

$$R_1 \cos \theta_2 - R_2 \cos \phi_2 + R_3 = \cos (\theta_2 - \phi_2) \tag{34}$$

$$R_1 \cos \theta_3 - R_2 \cos \phi_3 + R_3 = \cos (\theta_3 - \phi_3) \tag{35}$$

If we let

$$\theta_1 = \theta_0 + \alpha_1 \qquad \phi_1 = \phi_0 + \beta_1 \qquad \gamma_1 = \alpha_1 - \beta_1$$

$$\theta_2 = \theta_0 + \alpha_2 \qquad \phi_2 = \phi_0 + \beta_2 \qquad \gamma_2 = \alpha_2 - \beta_2$$

$$\theta_3 = \theta_0 + \alpha_3 \qquad \phi_3 = \phi_0 + \beta_3 \qquad \gamma_3 = \alpha_3 - \beta_3$$

Equations (1)–(4) may be written

$$R_1 \cos (\theta_0 + \alpha_0) - R_2 \cos (\phi_0 + \beta_0) + R_3 = \cos (\theta_0 - \phi_0 + \gamma_0) \tag{36}$$

$$R_1 \cos (\theta_0 + \alpha_1) - R_2 \cos (\phi_0 + \beta_1) + R_3 = \cos (\theta_0 - \phi_0 + \gamma_1) \tag{37}$$

$$R_1 \cos (\theta_0 + \alpha_2) - R_2 \cos (\phi_0 + \beta_2) + R_3 = \cos (\theta_0 - \phi_0 + \gamma_2) \tag{38}$$

$$R_1 \cos (\theta_0 + \alpha_3) - R_2 \cos (\phi_0 + \beta_3) + R_3 = \cos (\theta_0 - \phi_0 + \gamma_3) \tag{39}$$

Note: Ordinarily $\alpha_0 = \beta_0 = \gamma_0 = 0$. These symbols are included in Eq. (36) for the sake of symmetry.

From Eqs. (36)–(39) we can eliminate R_1, R_2, R_3, obtaining the following result:

$$\lambda_1 \tan^2 \theta_0 + \lambda_2 \tan \theta_0 + \lambda_3 = 0 \tag{40}$$

in which

$$\lambda_k = l_k + m_k \tan \phi_0 + n_k \tan^2 \phi_0 + p_k \tan^3 \phi_0 \; (k = 1, 2, 3) \tag{41}$$

$$l_1 = (C_3F_2 - C_2F_3) \tag{42}$$

$$l_2 = (A_2F_3 - A_3F_2) + (C_2E_3 - C_3E_2) \tag{43}$$

$$l_3 = (A_3E_2 - A_2E_3) \tag{44}$$

$$m_1 = (D_2F_3 - D_3F_2) + (C_2E_3 - C_3E_2) + (C_2H_3 - C_3H_2) \tag{45}$$

$$m_2 = (A_3E_2 - A_2E_3) + (A_3H_2 - A_2H_3) + (B_3F_2 - B_2F_3) - (C_3F_2 - C_2F_3) + (C_3G_2 - C_2G_3) + (D_3E_2 - D_2E_3) \tag{46}$$

$$m_3 = -(A_2F_3 - A_3F_2) + (A_2G_3 - A_3G_2) + (B_2E_3 - B_3E_2) \tag{47}$$

$$n_1 = (C_3G_2 - C_2G_3) + (D_3E_2 - D_2E_3) + (D_3H_2 - D_2H_3) \tag{48}$$

$$n_2 = (B_2E_3 - B_3E_2) + (B_2H_3 - B_3H_2) + (A_2G_3 - A_3G_2) - (D_2F_3 - D_3F_2) + (D_2G_3 - D_3G_2) - (C_2H_3 - C_3H_2) \tag{49}$$

$$n_3 = -(A_3H_2 - A_2H_3) - (B_3F_2 - B_2F_3) + (B_3G_2 - B_2G_3) \quad (50)$$

$$p_1 = (D_2G_3 - D_3G_2) \quad (51)$$

$$p_2 = (B_3G_2 - B_2G_3) - (D_3H_2 - D_2H_3) \quad (52)$$

$$p_3 = -(B_2H_3 - B_3H_2) \quad (53)$$

Each A, B, C, D, E, F, and G is the algebraic sum of six products of sines and cosines of α, β, and γ evaluated according to the following rules:

$$A_2 = \Sigma \cos \alpha_i \cos \beta_j \qquad (i,j = 0, 1, 2), (i \neq j) \quad (54a)$$

Terms are positive for

$$(i,j) = (0, 1), (1, 2) \text{ or } (2, 0)$$

Terms are negative for

$$(i,j) = (0, 2), (2, 1) \text{ or } (1, 0)$$

Negative i, j order — 0, 1, 2 — Positive i, j order

$$A_2 = (\cos \alpha_0 \cos \beta_1 - \cos \alpha_0 \cos \beta_2 + \cos \alpha_1 \cos \beta_2 - \cos \alpha_1 \cos \beta_0 + \cos \alpha_2 \cos \beta_0 - \cos \alpha_2 \cos \beta_1) \quad (54b)$$

$$B_2 = \Sigma \cos \alpha_i \sin \beta_j \quad (55)$$

$$C_2 = \Sigma \sin \alpha_i \cos \beta_j \quad (56)$$

$$D_2 = \Sigma \sin \alpha_i \sin \beta_j \quad (57)$$

$$E_2 = \Sigma \cos \beta_i \cos \gamma_j \quad (58)$$

$$F_2 = \Sigma \cos \beta_i \sin \gamma_j \quad (59)$$

$$G_2 = \Sigma \sin \beta_i \cos \gamma_j \quad (60)$$

$$H_2 = \Sigma \sin \beta_i \sin \gamma_j \quad (61)$$

A_3, B_3, . . . H_3 are evaluated in the same way as A_2, B_2, . . . H_2, with $i, j = 0, 1, 3$ instead of 0, 1, 2.

The starting point for design calculations would be specified values for α and β (hence known values for γ). The calculations would then follow this outline:

(1) Tabulate sines and cosines of α, β, and γ.

(2) Calculate all A, B, . . . H.

(3) Calculate all l, m, n, p.

(4) Assume a trial value for ϕ_0 and calculate λ's.

(5) Solve Eq. (40) for θ_0.

(6) Solve Eqs. (36), (37), and (38) for R_1, R_2, R_3. Check to see that Eq. 39 is satisfied.

(7) Determine link lengths from R_1, R_2, and R_3 (for an assumed length of one link).

Note: One step in the process of elimination used in arriving at Eq. (40) involved dividing by $\cos\phi_0$. Hence, $\phi_0 = 90$ deg. or 270 deg. must be treated separately. For this special case $\lambda_k = p_k$.

7.8 *Problem: 4-point approximation*

A 4-bar mechanism is to be designed to generate the function

$$y = -\frac{x}{8}(x+2)$$

in the range $0 < x < 6$. Both cranks are to rotate 90 deg. for this range of x. We choose to design for precision points at $x = 0$, 2, 4, and 6 and for opposite rotations of the two cranks.

(1) Tabulate x, y and α, β, γ at the required precision points.

TABLE I

	x	y	α	β	γ
0	0	0	0	0	0
1	2	−1	30°	−15°	45°
2	4	−3	60°	−45°	105°
3	6	−6	90°	−90°	180°

(2) Tabulate sines and cosines of α, β, γ.

TABLE II

	0	1	2	3
$\cos\alpha$	1	0.86603	0.50000	0
$\cos\beta$	1	0.96593	0.70711	0
$\cos\gamma$	1	0.70711	−0.25882	−1
$\sin\alpha$	0	0.50000	0.86603	1
$\sin\beta$	0	−0.25882	−0.70711	−1
$\sin\gamma$	0	0.70711	0.96593	0

TABLE III

	$E_3 = -0.22475$	$F_3 = +0.70711$	$G_3 = +0.22475$	$H_3 = +0.70711$
$A_2 = +0.02220$	−0.00429	+0.01570	+0.00499	+0.01570
$B_3 = -0.03468$	+0.00779	−0.02452	−0.00779	−0.02452
$C_3 = -0.11694$	+0.02628	−0.08269	−0.02628	−0.08269
$D_3 = -0.12941$	+0.02909	−0.09151	−0.02909	−0.09151

TABLE IV

	$E_2 = -0.04290$	$F_2 = +0.17421$	$G_2 = +0.11870$	$H_2 = +0.25000$
$A_3 = +0.09990$	−0.00429	+0.01740	+0.01186	+0.02498
$B_3 = -0.12485$	+0.00536	−0.02175	−0.01482	−0.03121
$C_3 = -0.46593$	+0.01999	−0.08117	−0.05531	−0.11648
$D_3 = -0.24118$	+0.01035	−0.04202	−0.02863	−0.06030

(3) Calculate the factors $A, B, \ldots, H$ and record in the spaces provided in Tables III and IV.

(4) Calculate the products of each of the factors A_2, B_2, C_2, D_2 with each of the factors E_3, F_3, G_3, H_3 and record in the body of Table III. Similarly fill in the body of Table IV.

(5) Calculate all l, m, n, p and record in Table V.

TABLE V

	1	2	3
l	+0.00152	+0.00459	+0.00071
m	−0.00940	−0.03653	−0.00273
n	−0.01655	+0.01750	−0.01907
p	−0.00046	−0.03824	−0.00669

(6) Choose a value for ϕ_0 and calculate λ's. For our first example we shall choose $\phi_0 = 0$. For this case

$$\lambda_1 = l_1 = 0.00152$$

$$\lambda_2 = l_2 = 0.00459$$

$$\lambda_3 = l_3 = 0.00071$$

Hence Eq. (9) is

$$0.00152 \tan^2 \theta_0 + 0.00459 \tan \phi_0 + 0.00071 = 0$$

or

$$\tan^2 \theta_0 + 3.020 \tan \phi_0 + 0.467 = 0$$

(7) Two designs are possible, corresponding to the two values obtained for θ_0. We shall work out the design for $\theta_0 = -70.7$ deg.

(8) All angles in our original equations, Eq. (32)–(35) or (36)–(39), are now known. These equations become

$$0.33051\,R_1 - 1.00000\,R_2 + R_3 = 0.33051$$
$$0.75813\,R_1 - 0.96593\,R_2 + R_3 = 0.90108$$
$$0.98261\,R_1 - 0.70711\,R_2 + R_3 = 0.82610$$
$$0.93544\,R_1 \qquad\qquad + R_3 = -0.35347$$

Solving the first three of these, we obtain

$$R_1 = 1.46$$
$$R_2 = -1.55$$
$$R_3 = -1.71$$

(9) Taking $d = 10$ in.

$$a = d/R_2 = -6.45 \text{ in.}$$
$$c = d/R_2 = 6.85 \text{ in.}$$
$$b = \sqrt{(d^2 + a^2 + c^2) - 2\,ca\,R_3} = 6.12 \text{ in.}$$

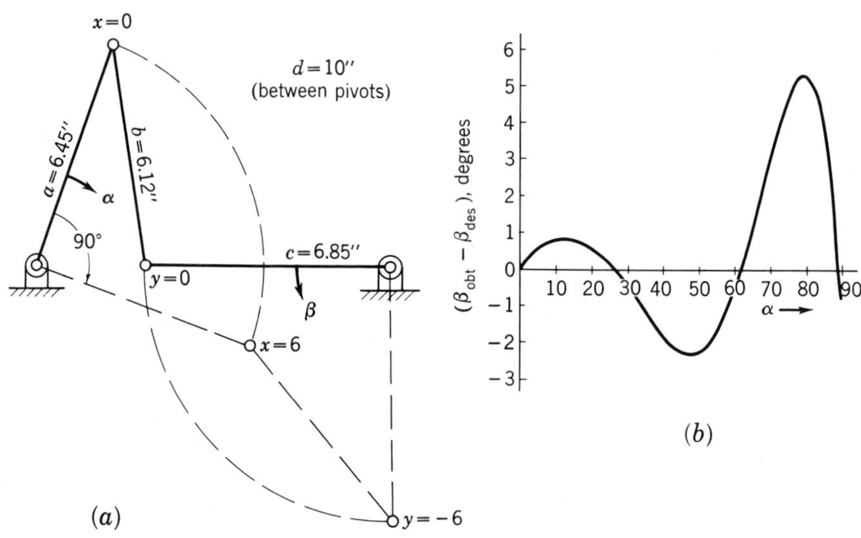

Fig. 7.5 (a) First mechanism designed to generate the function $y = -(x/8)(x+2)$. Based on choice of $\phi_0 = 0$. (b) Error curve for the above mechanism. The fact that the curve does not pass exactly through precision points results from carrying too few places through the calculations.

(10) The resulting mechanism is shown in Fig. 7.5(a). The error curve in Figure 7.5(b) shows that the precision points do not fall exactly at the design points. This is the result of carrying too few significant figures through the calculations.

7.9 *Second design:* $\phi_0 = -45$ *deg.*

If we choose $\phi_0 = -45$ deg. for the problem of the preceding article we find

$$\lambda_1 = -0.005175$$
$$\lambda_2 = 0.096864$$
$$\lambda_3 = -0.008949$$

from which $\theta_0 = 86.927$ deg. (one of the two solutions). Then

$$R_1 = 1.491 \qquad R_2 = 2.054 \qquad R_3 = 0.704$$

For $d = 10$ in. we find

$$a = 4.869 \text{ in.} \qquad c = 6.707 \text{ in.} \qquad b = 11.077 \text{ in.}$$

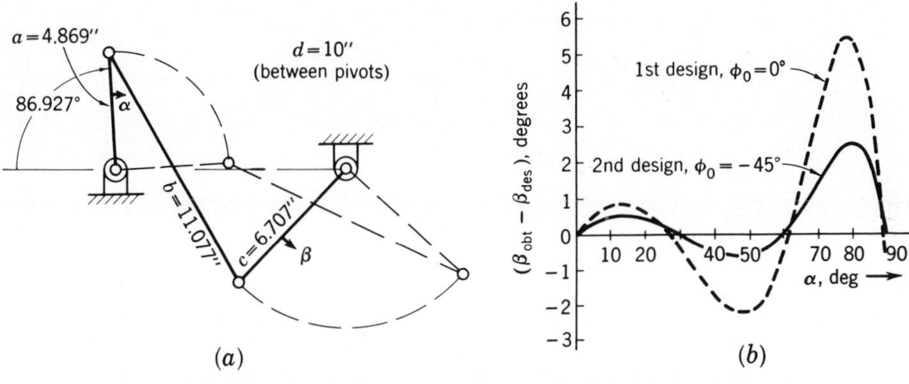

Fig. 7.6 (a) Second design of 4-bar to generate $y = -(x/8)(x+2)$. $\phi_0 = -45$ deg. (b) Error curve for the above mechanism compared with the previous design.

The resulting mechanism is shown in Fig. 7.6 along with the error curve. As a result of carrying more significant figures through the design computations, the precision points coincide with the design points more closely than in the previous solution.

We have also a more fortunate choice of ϕ_0 in this design, yielding a much smaller maximum error than in the previous design. For the same ϕ_0 a still better design might be found by choosing different locations for the precision points.

7.10 *Choice of precision points*

For most applications the best choice of precision points is that which gives the least maximum error within the range of variables for which we are designing. While we cannot predict exactly what spacing of precision points will give best results, some rough rules can be stated as a guide.

(1) Precision points near each end of the range should be more closely spaced than those in the middle of the range.

(2) Do not use precision points at the extreme ends of the range. (This rule was violated in Arts. 7.8 and 7.9.)

(3) Optimum spacing of precision points results in an error curve having equal absolute values for the maximum errors between precision points and at each end of the range.

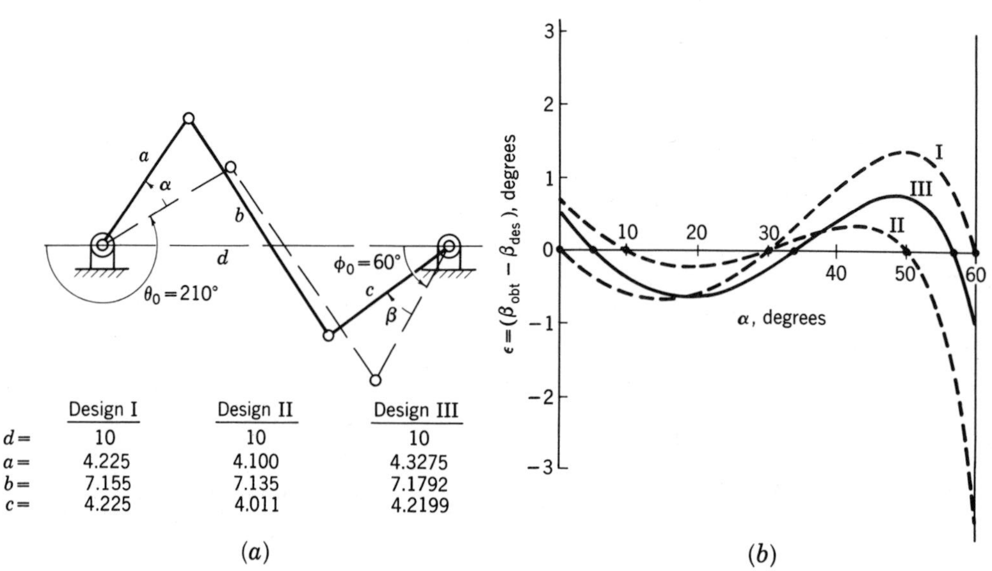

Fig. 7.7 (a) Three 4-bar mechanisms designed for the same function but with different spacing of three precision points used. (b) Error curves for the above mechanisms.

Figure 7.7 shows three mechanisms designed so that the cranks will have an angular-velocity ratio of -1 nearly constant over a 60-deg. range of motion. In each design θ (input angle) ranged from 210 to 270 deg. and $\phi = 0$ at $\theta = 270$ deg., but different spacings were used for the three precision points. The three error curves for this elementary example afford some support for the above rules.

Freudenstein (7) has given a method for systematically adjusting the precision points to approach the optimum condition.

7.11 *Higher-order approximations*

It is possible to go beyond the fourth-order and 4-point designs. If we leave ϕ as an unknown in Eq. (27), a fifth-order approximation can be worked out. If we leave ϕ_0 as an unknown in Eq. (40), a 5-point solution can be made.

If the scales (relations between function variables and crank displacements) are left as unknowns, it becomes theoretically possible to find seventh-order and 7-point designs. However, beyond the fourth-order and 4-point, the calculations become so extensive that making them is impractical unless they are programed for a high-speed digital computer. The reader who wishes to consider these higher approximations should consult Freudenstein's original papers.

Problems and Exercises

E7.1 Design a 4-bar mechanism, using Freudenstein's equation, such that the crank angles will be coordinated as follows:

θ, deg. . .	15	45	75
ϕ, deg. . .	40	60	90

Check graphically.

E7.2 Design a 4-bar mechanism, using Freudenstein's equation, such that the crank angles will be coordinated as follows:

θ, deg. . .	80	110	140
ϕ, deg. . .	-30	-50	-80

Check graphically.

E7.3 Design a 4-bar mechanism such that, in the design position, the angular-velocity ratio of the cranks (output/input) will be $+1.5$ constant to a 4th-order approximation. Use Freudenstein's equation. Check your design to discover within what range of motion the angular-velocity ratio remains within the limits 1.4–1.6.

E7.4 Design a 4-bar mechanism to generate the function $y = x^{3/2}$ in the vicinity of $x = 2$. Use Freudenstein's equation and make a 4th-order approximation. Plot the error curve for the range $1 < x < 3$.

E7.5 Design a 4-bar mechanism to generate the function $y = x^{3/2}$ in the range $1 < x < 3$. Use Freudenstein's equation and make a 4-point approximation. Plot the error curve. Compare with the design worked out in problem E7.4.

8

Finite displacements

8.1 *The general problem*

In this chapter we shall consider the general question: How can a rigid body in plane motion ("plane system") be guided through a finite number of specified positions by means of a lower-paired linkage? Partial answers, to be discussed in more detail in the following articles, are:

(1) *Two positions.* Pin joint the moving body to the fixed body at the pole (defined in the next article).

(2) *Three positions.* Make the moving body the coupler of a 4-bar mechanism. Any two points, A and B, belonging to the moving body can be used as crankpins. The crank pivots will be the centers, A_c and B_c, of the circles passing through the three positions of A and B, respectively.

(3) *Four positions.* Make the moving body the coupler of a 4-bar mechanism. Points belonging to the moving body and located on a certain curve (called the "circle point curve") have their four positions on circles. Any two points A and B on this curve can be used as crankpins.

(4) *Five positions.* A finite number of points belonging to the moving body will have five positions on circles. If two such points can be found, they can be used as crankpins in a 4-bar mechanism of which the moving body will be the coupler.

(5) *More than five positions.* No solution is to be expected using a single 4-bar mechanism.

The theory to be discussed is that originally presented by Burmester (8), with extensions by later investigators.

8.2 *Poles*

At the heart of the discussion will be the concept of the "pole," illustrated in Fig. 8.1. Given a rigid body in two positions, S_1 and S_2, the pole P_{12} (or P_{21}) is located at that point of the moving body (or an extension of it) for which positions 1 and 2 coincide. The moving body, in going from S_1 to S_2 (or S_2 to S_1), could (but does not necessarily) simply rotate around P_{12}.

To locate the pole pick two points, A and B, belonging to the moving body. Connect A_1 with A_2 and draw the perpendicular bisector of line A_1A_2. Likewise draw the perpendicular bisector of B_1B_2. These two perpendicular bisectors intersect at the pole P_{12}.

The reader will recognize the similarity between the pole for finite displacements and the instantaneous center (or "pole" for velocities). The following double statements bring out the comparison.

The pole for $\left\{\begin{matrix}\text{finite displacements}\\ \text{velocities}\end{matrix}\right\}$ is located at that point of the moving body having zero $\left\{\begin{matrix}\text{displacement}\\ \text{velocity}\end{matrix}\right\}$.

The $\left\{\begin{matrix}\text{finite}\\ \text{instantaneous}\end{matrix}\right\}$ motion of the body may be considered as rotation around the pole for $\left\{\begin{matrix}\text{finite displacements}\\ \text{velocities}\end{matrix}\right\}$ for the purpose of calculating $\left\{\begin{matrix}\text{displacements}\\ \text{velocities}\end{matrix}\right\}$.

The pole as defined for finite displacements becomes the instantaneous center, or pole for velocities, in the limit as the finite displacement is made to approach zero.

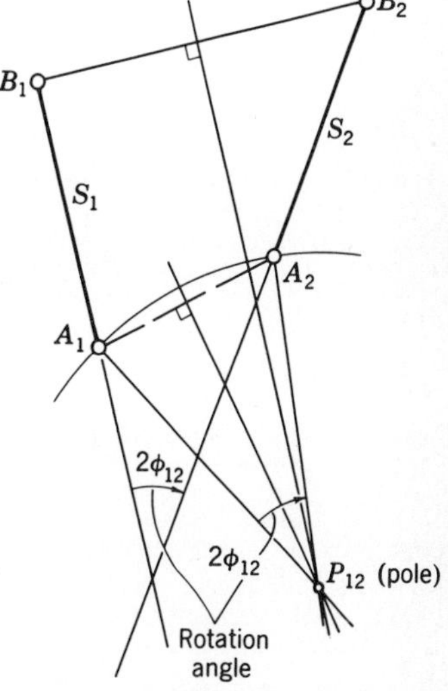

Fig. 8.1 A moving body in two positions, showing the rotation angle $2\phi_{12}$ and the pole P_{12}.

8.3 *Rotation angle*

The angle through which a body turns in going from one position to another will be called the "rotation angle" and will be designated as shown in Fig. 8.1. The symbol ϕ will be used for one-half the rotation angle, for reasons to appear later. Hence, 2ϕ will be the full rotation angle. Subscripts will indicate rotation *from* one position *to* another. Thus $2\phi_{12}$ is the angle through which the body rotates in going from position 1 to position 2. To indicate the rotation angle from position 2 to position 1, we would write $2\phi_{21}$. Notice that

$$2\phi_{12} + 2\phi_{21} = 360 \text{ deg.}$$

Hence

$$\phi_{12} + \phi_{21} = 180 \text{ deg.}$$

8.4 *The pole triangle*

If we consider a body in three successive positions, S_1, S_2, and S_3, three poles, P_{12}, P_{23}, P_{31}, are involved. These three poles are the vertexes of the pole triangle. (See Fig. 8.2) In the theory to follow, this triangle plays a major role.

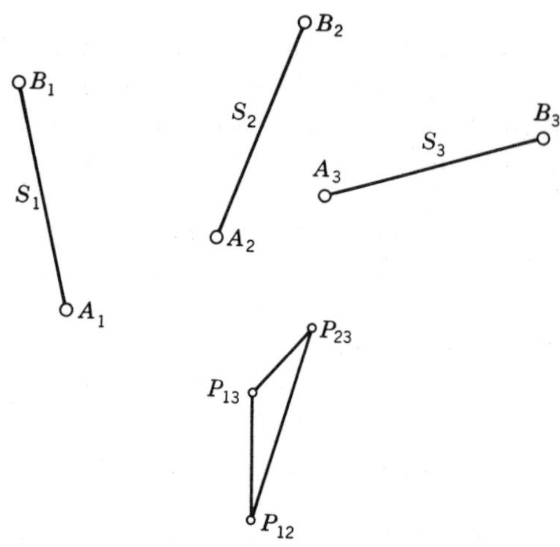

Fig. 8.2 A body in three positions. The three poles are the vertexes of the "pole triangle."

An important property of the pole triangle is the fact that the interior angles are the half rotation angles, i.e., the interior angle at P_{12} is ϕ_{12}, at P_{23} the interior angle is ϕ_{23}, and at P_{31} the interior angle is ϕ_{31}. Proof of this can be worked out by the following argument, referring to Fig. 8.3.

(a) Consider that point belonging to the moving body and located at P_{23} in positions 2 and 3. In position 1 this point will occupy a location which we designate P^1_{23}.

(b) Since the entire body can be carried from position 1 to position 2 by rotation around P_{12}, point P^1_{23} must lie on an arc through P_{23} and centered at P_{12}.

(c) Since the entire body can be carried from position 1 to position 3 by rotation around P_{31}, point P^1_{23} must lie on an arc through P_{23} and centered at P_{31}.

(d) Hence, P^1_{23} and P_{23} are symmetrically located with respect to line $P_{12}P_{31}$.

(e) Since the full rotation angle from position 1 to position 2 is angle $P^1_{23}P_{12}P_{23}$, the interior angle of the pole

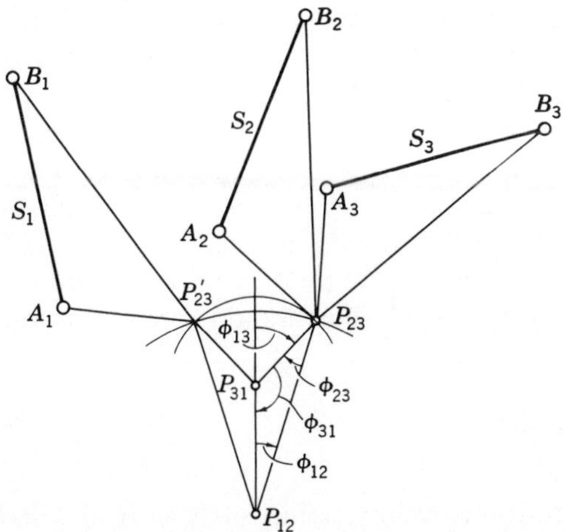

Fig. 8.3 Reference diagram for showing that the interior angles of the pole triangle are the half rotation angles.

triangle at vertex P_{12} is ϕ_{12}, the half rotation angle.

(f) Since the full rotation angle from position 1 to position 3 is angle $P^1_{23}P_{31}P_{23}$, the exterior angle at P_{31} is ϕ_{13}. Hence the interior angle at P_{31} is ϕ_{31}. ($\phi_{13} + \phi_{31} = 180$ deg.)

(g) Now, successive rotations from 1 to 2, 2 to 3, and 3 to 1 make a full revolution, or

$$\phi_{12} + \phi_{23} + \phi_{31} = 180 \text{ deg.}$$

Since the interior angles of any triangle total 180 deg., and since ϕ_{12} and ϕ_{31} have already been shown to be two of the interior angles of the pole triangle, ϕ_{23} must be the third interior angle.

8.5 *Problem: finding A_2 and A_3, knowing A_1 and the pole triangle*

Given the location A_1 of one point belonging to a body moved through three specified positions and the pole triangle for the motion, determine locations A_2 and A_3 for the given point. Refer to Fig. 8.4.

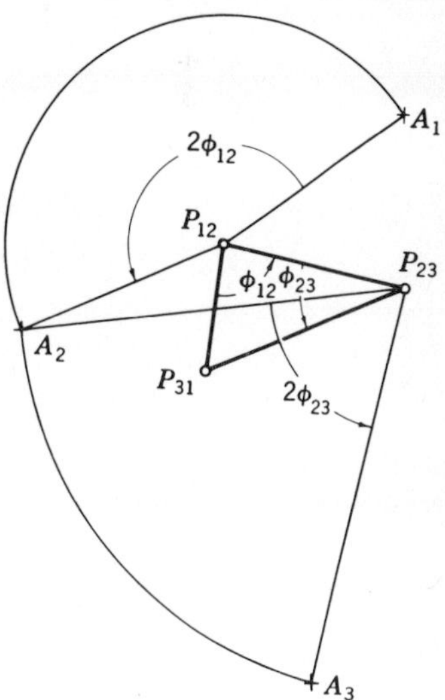

Fig. 8.4 A solution to the problem of finding A_2 and A_3, given A_1 and the pole triangle.

SOLUTION

(1) Identify the angle ϕ_{12} in the pole triangle. In this example this is the *counterclockwise* interior angle at P_{12}. The rule for determining sense is as follows:

The sense of angle ϕ_{12} is that which would carry line $P_{12}P_{31}$ (common subscript 1) around P_{12} toward line $P_{12}P_{23}$ (common subscript 2).

Similarly identify angle ϕ_{23}. The sense of this is that which would carry line $P_{23}P_{12}$ (common subscript 2) around P_{23} toward line $P_{23}P_{31}$ (common subscript 3).

(2) Knowing the angle ϕ_{12}, we know the rotation angle $2\phi_{12}$. Rotate line $P_{12}A_1$ around P_{12} through this angle. This will carry A_1 into A_2. Similarly rotate line $P_{23}A_2$ through angle $2\phi_{23}$ around P_{23}. This will carry A_2 into A_3.

(3) As a check, identify angle ϕ_{13} and rotate line $P_{31}A_1$ through angle $2\phi_{13}$ around P_{31}. This should carry A_1 into A_3.

8.6 *The center system*

The three positions of any point, such as B in Fig. 8.5, belonging to the moving body fall on a circle with center at B_c. The figure shows how B_c can be located by drawing perpendicular bisectors of lines B_1B_2 and B_1B_3. All points such as B_c make up the "center system."

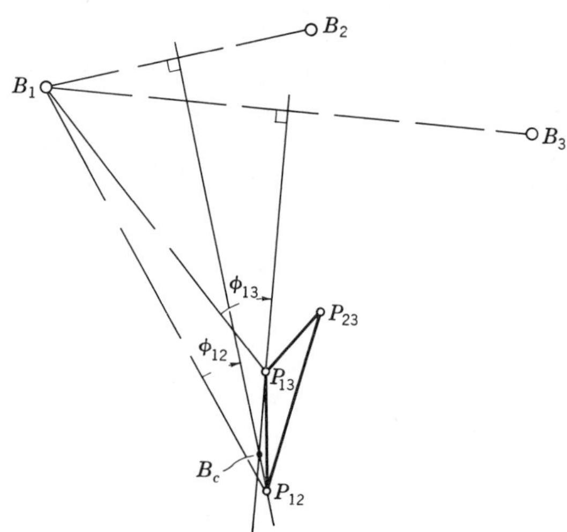

Fig. 8.5 B_c, the center of the circle which would pass through B_1, B_2, and B_3, is a point of the center system.

Since the perpendicular bisectors of B_1B_2 and B_1B_3 contain poles P_{12} and P_{31}, respectively, there is a relation between the locations of B_1, B_2, B_3, B_c and the pole triangle. In particular, if we draw a line from P_{12} to B_1, the angle from this line to the perpendicular bisector of B_1B_2 is ϕ_{12}. Likewise the angle from $P_{31}B_1$ to the perpendicular bisector of B_1B_3 is ϕ_{13}. These relations will be used to solve a problem in the next article.

8.7 *Problem: finding E_1, knowing E_c and pole triangle*

Given the pole triangle for a body moved through three positions and one point, E_c, of the center system, find the location of the corresponding point E_1 belonging to the moving body in position 1. Refer to Fig. 8.6.

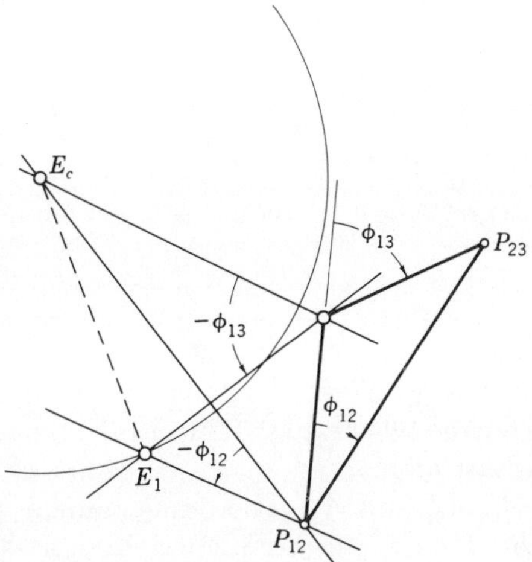

Fig. 8.6 With the pole triangle given, we can locate E_1 corresponding to any point E_c of the center system.

SOLUTION

(1) Identify angles ϕ_{12} and ϕ_{13}.

(2) Connect E_c with P_{12} and draw a line through P_{12} at angle $-\phi_{12}$ with line $P_{12}E_c$. According to the observations of the previous article, E_1 must be on this last line drawn.

(3) Similarly, E_1 must fall on the line through P_{31} at angle $-\phi_{13}$ with line $P_{31}E_c$.

Remembering that E_c is the center of the circle through E_1, E_2, and E_3, we could check the results of the above solution by finding E_2 and E_3, as explained in Art. 8.5.

8.8 *Problem: three-position design of a guiding linkage, crankpins specified*

The body shown in Fig. 8.7(a) is to be guided through the three positions indicated. Guiding is to be accomplished by two cranks pin-jointed to the moving body at A and B. Complete the design of the mechanism.

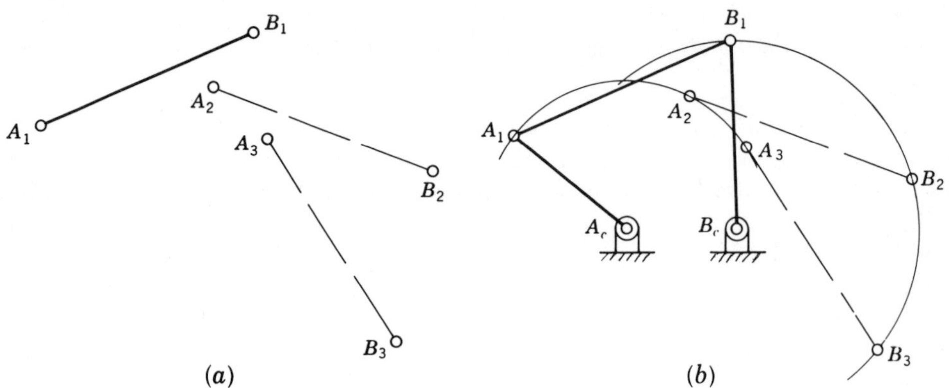

Fig. 8.7 (a) Three positions of a moving body, to be guided by cranks pinned at A and B. (b) The designed mechanism.

SOLUTION

This is a fairly trivial problem. To complete the design we must find the pivots for the two cranks. The crank pinned to the moving body at A must be pivoted at A_c, the center of the circle passing through A_1, A_2, and A_3. The crank pinned at B must be pivoted at B_c. Hence the completed design is as shown in Fig. 8.7(b).

8.9 *Problem: three-position design of a guiding linkage, crank pivots specified*

The body shown in Fig. 8.8(a) is to be guided through the three positions indicated. Guiding is to be accomplished by two cranks pivoted at D_c and E_c. Complete the design of the mechanism.

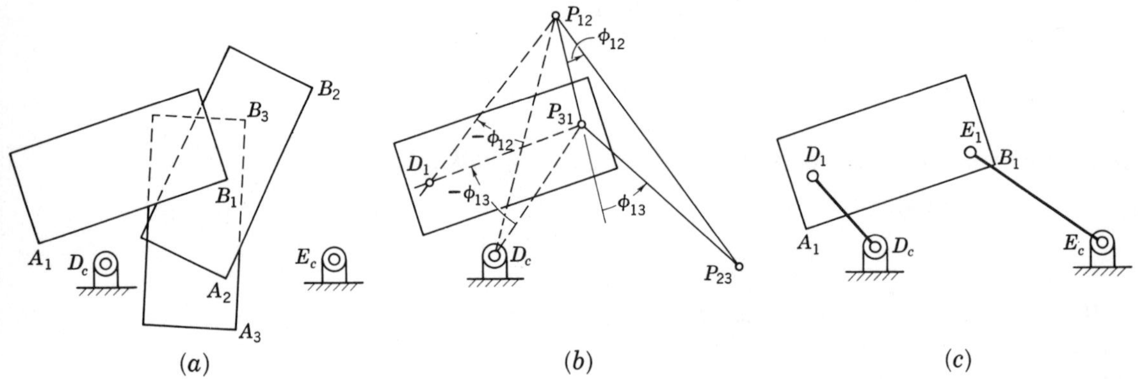

Fig. 8.8 (a) Three positions of a moving body, to be guided by cranks pivoted at D_c and E_c. (b) Finding D_1 corresponding to D_c. (c) The completed mechanism.

SOLUTION

(1) To complete the design, we must locate points D and E of the moving body, corresponding to the specified D_c and E_c. As the first step we determine the pole triangle. [Fig. 8.8(b)].

(2) Having the pole triangle, we can find D_1 and E_1 corresponding to the specified D_c and E_c by the method described in Art. 8.7.

(3) The completed design is as shown in Fig. 8.8(c).

8.10 *Moving points having three positions on straight lines*

Certain points belonging to a body moved through three specified positions will have their three positions on straight lines. To investigate the location of such points we reason as follows.

(1) Referring to Fig. 8.9, assume that we have already determined the pole triangle for the specified motion.

(2) The circle through the three positions of one of the points we are investigating has infinite radius, i.e., if we call such a point D, then the corresponding point, D_c, of the center system lies at infinity.

(3) We select a direction line d–d and propose to locate a point D of the moving body such that D_1, D_2, and D_3 will fall on a line parallel to d–d.

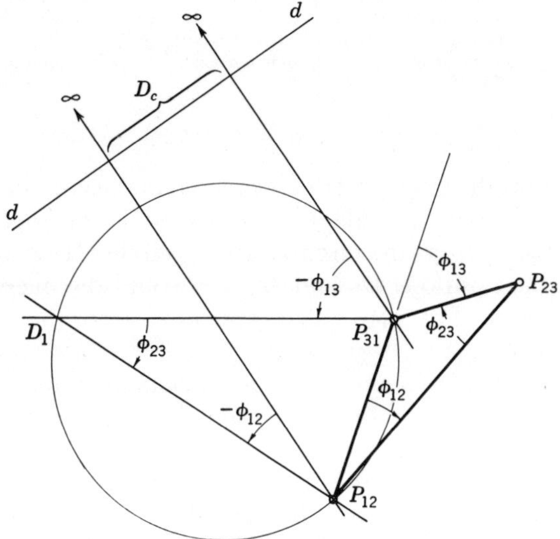

Fig. 8.9 The circle shown contains position 1 of all points which have their three positions on straight lines, i.e., on circles of infinite radius.

(4) D_c will be at infinity in a direction perpendicular to *d—d*. We draw lines from P_{12} and P_{13} toward D_c.

(5) We now apply the construction described in Art. 8.7 to locate D_1. Through P_{12} and P_{31} we draw lines at angles $-\phi_{12}$ and $-\phi_{13}$, respectively, with the lines $P_{12}D_c$ and $P_{31}D_c$. The intersection locates D_1.

(6) The two lines locating D_1 intersect at angle ϕ_{23}. This would be the case regardless of the inclination selected for direction line *d–d*.

(7) We conclude that the locus of all points such as D_1 is the circle shown in Fig. 8.9, having $P_{12}P_{31}$ as a chord subtending the central angle $2\phi_{23}$.

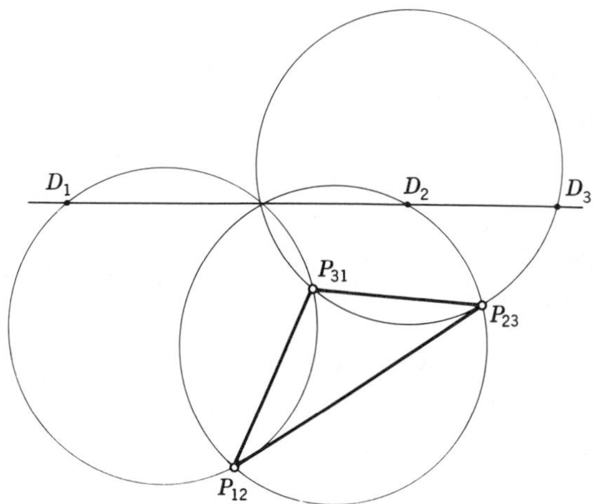

Fig. 8.10 D_1, D_2, D_3 respectively lie on the circles with chords $P_{12}P_{31}$, $P_{12}P_{23}$, $P_{23}P_{31}$. The three circles have the same diameter, which is equal to the diameter of the circle that would circumscribe the pole triangle.

Notice that the circle just determined is of the correct size to circumscribe the pole triangle, but is centered on the opposite side of chord $P_{12}P_{31}$ from the circumscribing circle. If we were to investigate the positions D_2 and D_3, we would discover the situation pictured in Fig. 8.10. The three circles are the same size.

In the finite displacement problem, points having their three positions on straight lines correspond to points having paths of infinite radius of curvature in the type of problem discussed in Chapter 5. In the limit, if we let the finite displacements we are discussing in this chapter approach zero, the circles shown in Fig. 8.10 coalesce and become the inflection circle.

8.11 *Problem: three-position design of a guiding linkage, straight guides*

The body shown in Fig. 8.11 is to be guided through the three specified positions by means of two sliders pin-jointed to the moving body and directed by straight guide surfaces. Determine one design for the mechanism.

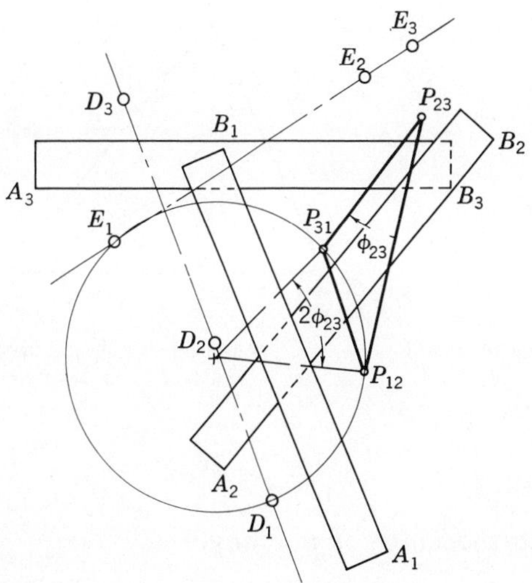

Fig. 8.11 Problem of Art. 8.11. The body given in three successive positions is to be guided by two sliders moving on straight guides.

SOLUTION

(1) We start by determining the pole triangle (construction details not shown) and identifying the angle ϕ_{23}.

(2) We construct the circle having central angle $2\phi_{23}$ subtended by chord $P_{12}P_{31}$ (remembering that the circle needed is the one which *does not* circumscribe the pole triangle).

(3) Any two points belonging to the moving body and located, in position 1, on the circle just drawn will have their three positions on straight lines and therefore will be suitable points to which to pin joint the sliders.

(4) For one design we select the two points D_1 and E_1 and proceed to find D_2, D_3, E_2, and E_3. This serves as a check on the accuracy of the graphical work and also establishes the lines of travel for pins D and E.

(5) The completed design is as shown in Fig. 8.12.

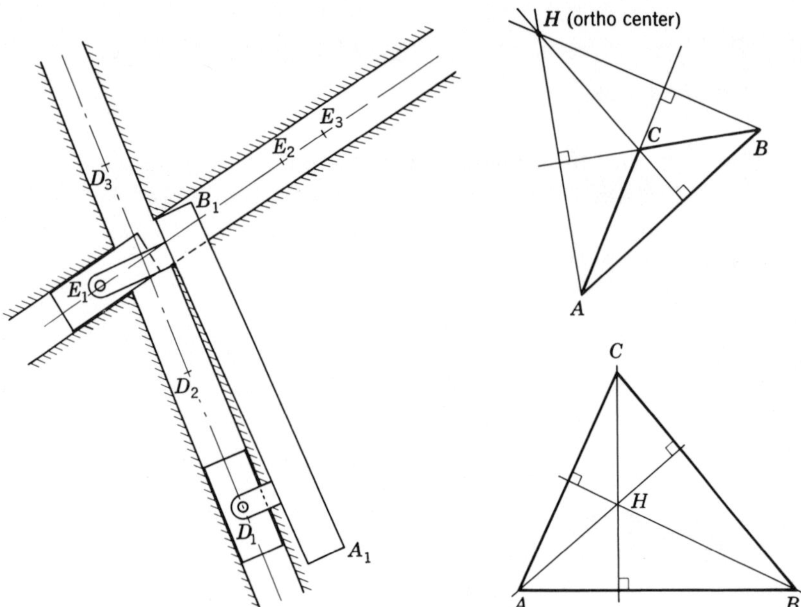

Fig. 8.12 Problem of Art. 8.11. The mechanism as designed from the layout of Fig. 8.11.

Fig. 8.13 The orthocenter, H, of a triangle.

8.12 *Geometry: orthocenter of a triangle*

As illustrated in Fig. 8.13, the lines through the three vertexes of a triangle perpendicular to the opposite sides intersect in a common point, H, called the orthocenter of the triangle. The orthocenter may fall either inside or outside the triangle, or at a vertex (in the case of a right triangle).

The orthocenter of a pole triangle has kinematic significance which will be explained in the next article.

8.13 *Orthocenter of a pole triangle*

Figure 8.14 shows a pole triangle with its orthocenter, H, located by drawing lines through vertexes P_{12} and P_{31} perpendicular to the opposite sides. The first significant thing to notice is that angle $P_{12}HP_{31}$ is equal to ϕ_{23}. Hence H is located on the circle with chord $P_{12}P_{31}$ subtending central angle $2\phi_{23}$. This is precisely the circle found in Art. 8.10 to be the locus, in position 1, of all moving points having three positions on straight lines.

In Fig. 8.15 a point D_1 has been arbitrarily selected on the circle passing through H, P_{31}, and P_{12}, and D_2 has been

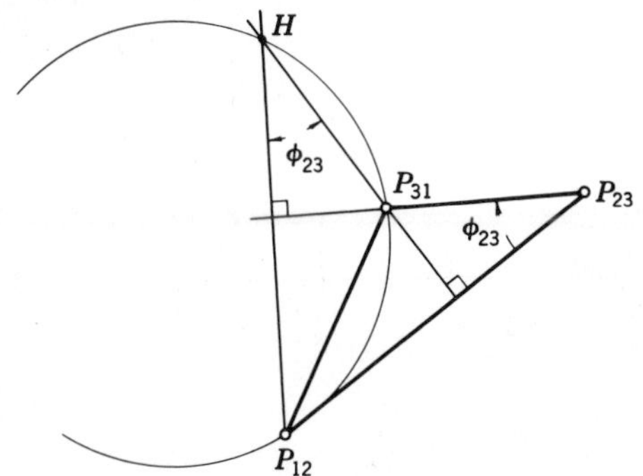

Fig. 8.14 The orthocenter, H, of a pole triangle, falls on the circle containing, in position 1, all points having their three positions on straight lines.

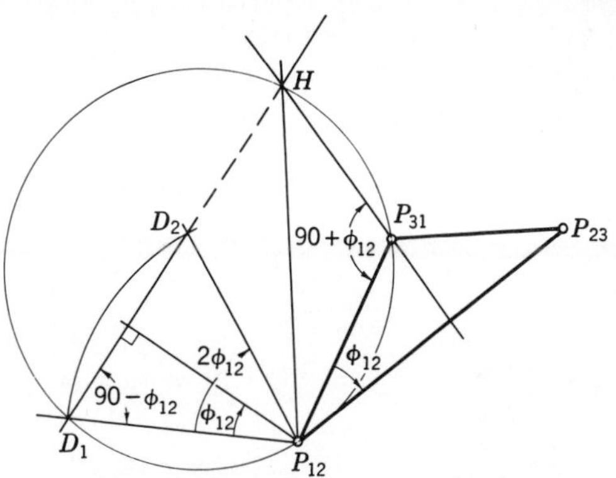

Fig. 8.15 Let D_1 be any point whose three positions fall on a straight line. The straight line contains the orthocenter, H, of the pole triangle.

located by rotating line $P_{12}D_1$ around P_{12} through angle $2\phi_{12}$. Notice that angle $P_{12}D_1D_2$ is $90 - \phi_{12}$.

Now verify that angle $P_{12}P_{31}H$ is $90 + \phi_{12}$. Angle $P_{12}D_1H$ must therefore be $90 - \phi_{12}$ since the quadrilateral $P_{12}D_1HP_{31}$ is inscribed in a circle. Since angle $P_{12}D_1H$ is identical with angle $P_{12}D_1D_2$, the line D_1D_2 extended must pass through H.

We conclude that, if three positions are specified for a body in plane motion, those points belonging to the moving body and having their three positions on straight lines are located, in position 1, on the circle passing through poles P_{12} and P_{31} and the orthocenter of the pole triangle. Furthermore, all the straight lines just referred to intersect at the orthocenter of the pole triangle.

8.14 *The point $\bar{A}$*

Here we shall consider another way of solving the kind of problem considered in Art. 8.5. In Fig. 8.16 we are given the pole triangle and position A_1 of a point belonging to the moving body. The problem is to determine A_2 and A_3.

We start by reflecting A_1 about line $P_{12}P_{31}$ to locate the point labelled $\bar{A}$. We then reflect $\bar{A}$ about line $P_{12}P_{23}$ to locate A_2. To prove that we have truly found A_2 we reason as follows.

(1) The construction as described makes

$$P_{12}A_1 = P_{12}\bar{A} = P_{12}A_2$$

Hence a circle can be drawn as shown.

(2) The construction makes angle

$$A_1\bar{A}A_2 = \phi_{12}$$

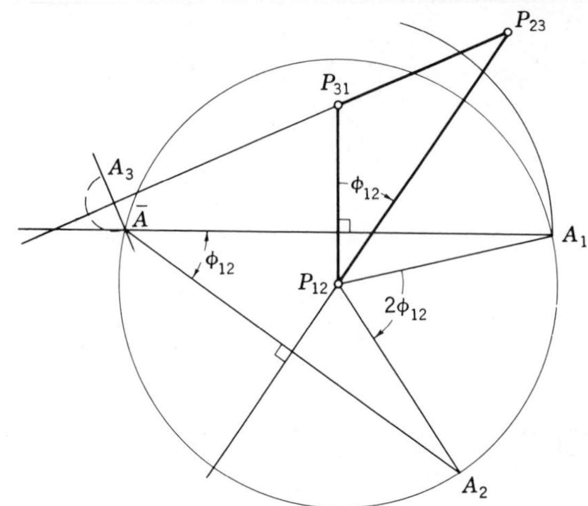

Fig. 8.16 The point $\bar{A}$ is the reflection of A_1 about $P_{12}P_{31}$, of A_2 about $P_{12}P_{23}$, and of A_3 about $P_{31}P_{23}$.

Hence the central angle $A_1P_{12}A_2$ is $2\phi_{12}$.

(3) Therefore we have correctly located A_2 at the proper rotation angle from A_1.

If $\bar{A}$ were reflected around line $P_{31}P_{23}$ we would find that we had correctly located A_3.

8.15 *Reflections of the orthocenter of the pole triangle, Fig. 8.17*

If the orthocenter of a pole triangle is reflected around the three sides of the triangle, we obtain three points, H_1, H_2,

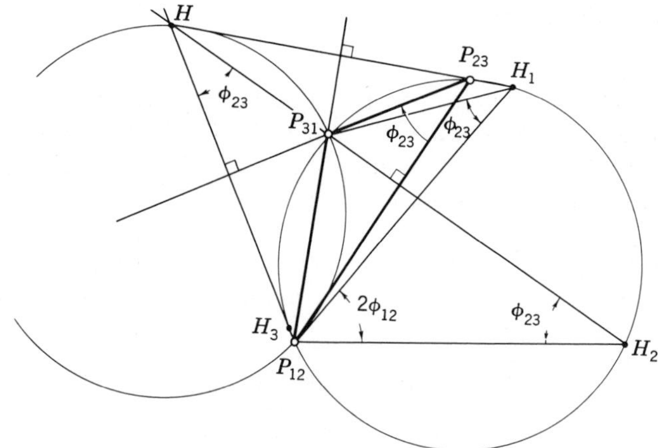

Fig. 8.17 H_1, H_2, and H_3 are reflections of the orthocenter H about the different sides of the pole triangle. H_1, H_2, and H_3 lie on the circle circumscribing the pole triangle.

and H_3, as illustrated in Fig. 8.17. From the previous article we know that H_2 and H_3 are the second and third positions of a point, initially at H_1, belonging to the moving body. A little study of the angles involved will show that H_1, H_2, and H_3 all lie on the circle circumscribing the pole triangle.

8.16 *Three positions of a moving line*

So far we have been discussing three finitely separated positions of a body in plane motion, with particular reference to the motions of *points* belonging to the moving body. We now wish to consider the motion of a *line* belonging to the moving body.

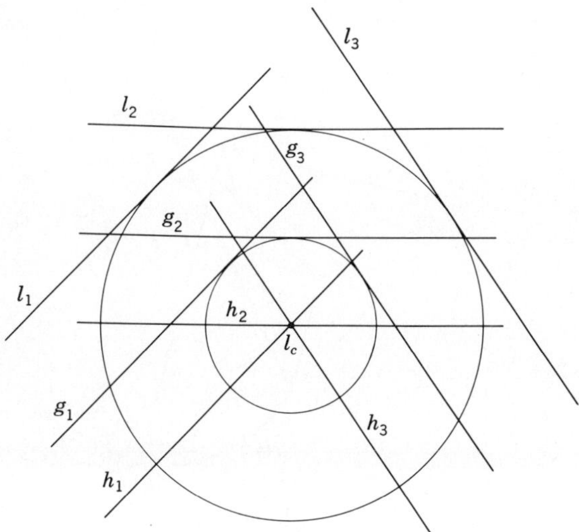

Fig. 8.18 Parallel lines belonging to a moving body in three positions. These lines are tangent to circles of different radii but with common center, l_c. Line h is tangent to circle of zero radius, i.e., h_1, h_2, h_3 intersect at point l_c.

Figure 8.18 shows a line l belonging to a moving body in three positions, l_1, l_2, and l_3. These three positions of l are tangent to a circle with center l_c. A cylindrical surface with center l_c could serve as one guide for the moving body.

The three positions of any other line, such as g, parallel to l, are also tangent to a circle with center l_c, but of different radius (in this case smaller) than the circle tangent to l_1, l_2, l_3. We are especially interested in the line h. The three positions h_1, h_2, h_3 are tangent to a circle with center l_c and zero radius, i.e., the three positions of line h intersect at a common point l_c.

We now wish to show that, if the three positions of a moving line (such as h_1, h_2, h_3 in Fig. 8.18) intersect at a common point, then (1) the point of intersection, l_c, is on the circle circumscribing the pole triangle, and (2) h_1, h_2, h_3 contain, respectively, the orthocenter reflections H_1, H_2, H_3 discussed in Art. 8.15.

Fig. 8.19 shows a pole triangle, the orthocenter H, its reflections H_1, H_2, H_3, and the circle circumscribing the pole triangle. We reason as follows.

(1) Pass any line, h_1, through H_1. Let this be the initial position of a line belonging to the moving body.

(2) As the body moves to positions 2 and 3, point H_1 of the body will be carried to H_2 and H_3, respectively. Therefore, h_2 will pass through H_2, and h_3 will pass through H_3.

(3) Line h_2 must make angle $2\phi_{12}$ with h_1 since the body rotates through angle $2\phi_{12}$ in going from position 1 to position 2. Lines h_1 and h_2 intersect at a point which we tentatively label l_c. Angle $H_1l_cH_2$ is $2\phi_{12}$.

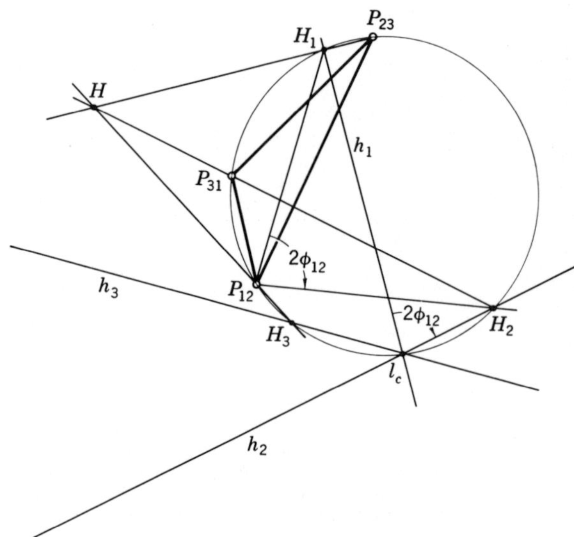

Fig. 8.19 Diagram for the argument in Art. 8.16 to the effect that the locus of centers of circles tangent to three positions of moving lines is the circle circumscribing the pole triangle.

(4) We already know that angle $H_1P_{12}H_2$ is $2\phi_{12}$, since H_1 is carried into H_2 by rotation around P_{12}. Hence, l_c must lie on the circle through H_1, P_{12}, and H_2, i.e., the circle circumscribing the pole triangle.

(5) Similar reasoning concerning the intersections of h_1 with h_3 and h_2 with h_3 and concerning the angles $H_3l_cH_1$ and

$H_2 l_c H_3$ will show that h_1, h_2, and h_3 intersect at the common point l_c on the circle circumscribing the pole triangle.

Our major conclusion is that the locus of centers of circles tangent to three positions of moving lines is the circle circumscribing the pole triangle. This circle plays the same part in the study of finite displacements as does the cuspidal circle in our earlier study of infinitesimal displacements (path curvature, etc., Chapter 5). In the limit, as the finite displacements approach zero, the circle circumscribing the pole triangle approaches the cuspidal circle. The points H_1, H_2, H_3 coalesce and approach the cuspidal pole.

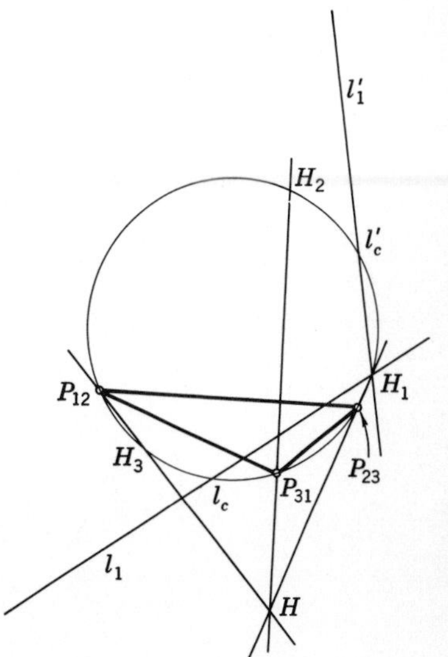

Fig. 8.20 Partial layout for the design problem of Art. 8.17. A body whose motion is defined by the given pole triangle is to be guided by two fixed pins working in straight slots of the moving body.

8.17 *Problem: three-position design with fixed pin guides*

A body in plane motion is to be guided through three positions, the displacements being defined by the pole triangle shown in Fig. 8.20. Guiding is to be accomplished by two fixed pins projecting into straight slots cut in the moving body. Determine suitable pin locations and orientations of the slots.

SOLUTION

(1) We first find the orthocenter of the pole triangle and its reflections, H_1, H_2, H_3. We also draw the circle circumscribing the pole triangle.

(2) Through H_1 we draw two lines, l_1 and l_1', cutting the circle at l_c and l_c' respectively.

(3) From the discussion of the previous article we know that the lines l_1 and l_1', considered as attached to the moving body, will continue to pass through l_c and l_c' respectively when the body is moved to positions 2 and 3. The body will therefore be properly guided if we establish pins at l_c and l_c' projecting into slots along l and l'. The design, with the body in position 1, is shown in Fig. 8.21.

8.18 *Points having four positions on circles*

If we consider *four* specified positions of a moving body, the four positions of an arbitrarily selected point belonging to the body will not, in general, fall on a circle. However, we shall show that there are some points whose four positions do fall on circles. Such points would be suitable locations for crankpins, with crank pivots at the circle centers, for guiding the body through the specified positions.

In Fig. 8.22, let point B be a point belonging to a moving body and so chosen that its four positions, B_1, B_2, B_3, B_4, fall on a circle with center B_c. In dealing with four positions, six poles

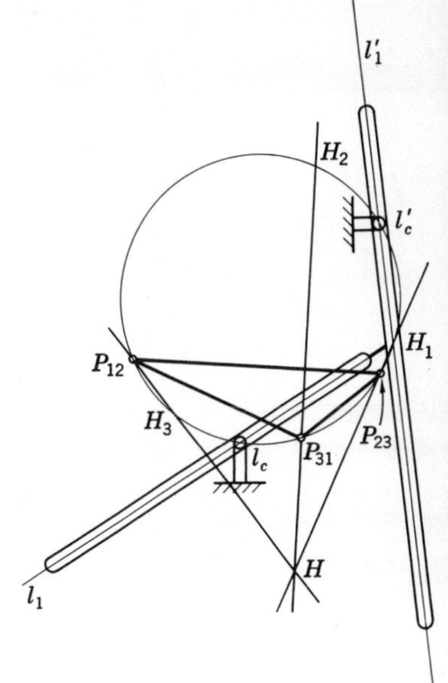

Fig. 8.21 A completed solution to the design problem of Art. 8.17.

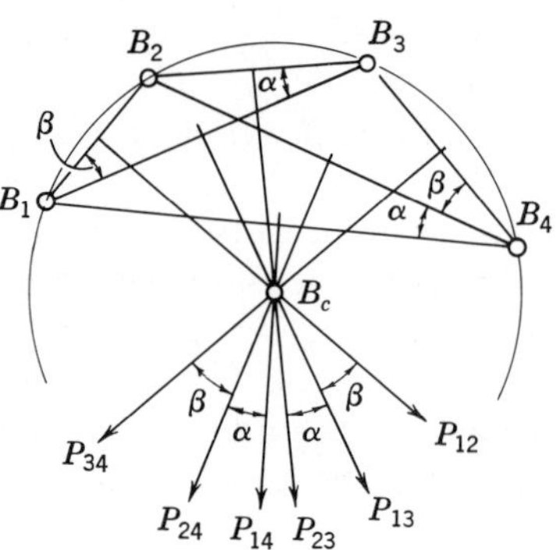

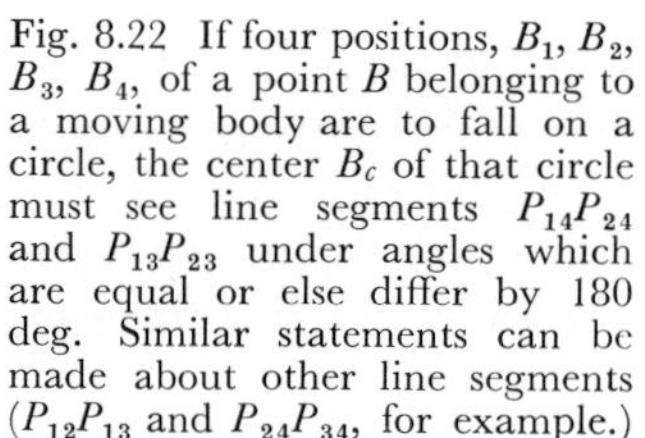
Fig. 8.22 If four positions, B_1, B_2, B_3, B_4, of a point B belonging to a moving body are to fall on a circle, the center B_c of that circle must see line segments $P_{14}P_{24}$ and $P_{13}P_{23}$ under angles which are equal or else differ by 180 deg. Similar statements can be made about other line segments ($P_{12}P_{13}$ and $P_{24}P_{34}$, for example.)

are involved—P_{12}, P_{13}, P_{14}, P_{23}, P_{24}, and P_{34}. In Fig. 8.22 we can locate lines which pass through these poles. For example, the perpendicular bisector of B_1B_2 passes through P_{12}, the perpendicular bisector of B_2B_4 passes through P_{24}, etc. These perpendicular bisectors all pass through B_c.

In Fig. 8.22 the lines running toward the various poles are shown with arrow heads. This does not mean that the poles are necessarily located in the sense of the arrows along these lines. Pole P_{12}, for example, instead of being below B_c might be above it.

A study of the angles between the various lines in Fig. 8.22 enables us to formulate statements of the following kind:

> *If four positions, B_1, B_2, B_3, B_4, of a point B belonging to a moving body are to fall on a circle, the center B_c of that circle must see line segments $P_{14}P_{24}$ and $P_{13}P_{23}$ under angles which are equal or else differ by* 180 *deg.*

The same statement could be made concerning line segments $P_{24}P_{34}$ and $P_{12}P_{13}$, as well as other pairs. All such statements will be put in one compact form after the introduction of some additional terminology in the next article.

8.19 *Opposite pole quadrangles*

Two poles whose subscripts do not contain a common numeral are called "opposite poles." For example, P_{12} and P_{34} are opposite poles. Two pairs of opposite poles form an opposite pole quadrangle. "Adjacent poles" are those whose subscripts do contain a common numeral. The "sides" of an opposite pole quadrangle are the lines joining adjacent poles. Fig. 8.23 shows some conceivable configurations of opposite pole quadrangles.

We can now make the following statement:

If the four positions of a point B, belonging to a body moved through four specified positions, are to fall on a circle, the center B_c of that circle must see the opposite sides of an opposite pole quadrangle under angles which are equal or else differ by 180 *deg.*

The converse is also true. If a point B_c does see the opposite sides of an opposite pole quadrangle under angles which are equal or else differ by 180 deg., B_c is the center of a circle passing through the four positions of some point B belonging to the moving body.

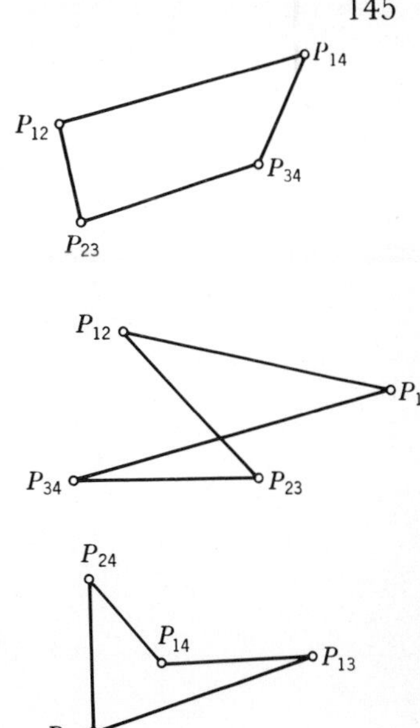

Fig. 8.23 Some possible configurations of opposite pole quadrangles.

8.20 *Center curve, and circle-point curve*

All points such as B_c discussed in the previous two articles belong to the *center curve* drawn on the fixed reference body. The corresponding points B belong to the *circle-point curve* drawn on the moving body.

Figure 8.24 shows a way to plot points on the center curve, given an opposite pole quadrangle.

(1) We choose to use the opposite sides $P_{12}P_{23}$ and $P_{14}P_{34}$. (We could just as well have chosen to use $P_{12}P_{14}$ and $P_{23}P_{34}$.)

(2) With $P_{12}P_{23}$ as a chord we draw a circle of arbitrary radius. With $P_{14}P_{34}$ as a chord we draw another circle whose

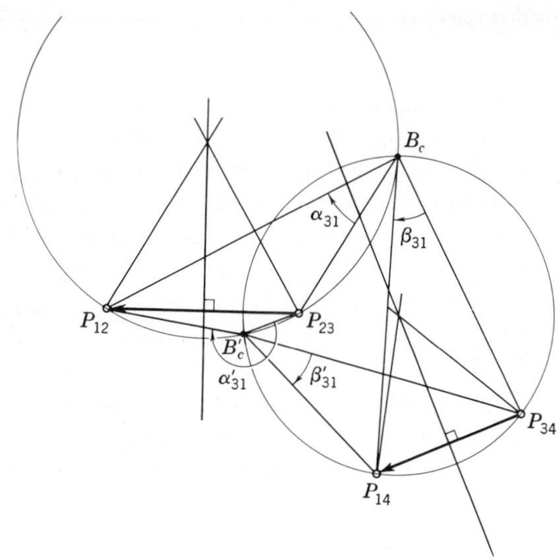

Fig. 8.24 Illustrating the construction described in Art. 8.20 for finding points of the center curve.

radius is to that of the first circle as the length of chord $P_{14}P_{34}$ is to the length of chord $P_{12}P_{23}$.

The two chords should be thought of as directed line segments. For the moment we forget the common subscript in the poles P_{12} and P_{23}, so that we think of P_1 and P_3. As we face P_1 from P_3, the center of the first circle drawn is on our right. Likewise, for the moment, we forget the common subscript in the poles P_{14} and P_{34}, so that we again think of P_1 and P_3. As we again face P_1 from P_3, the center of the second circle we drew should also be on our right.

(3) The two circles intersect in two points, B_c and B_c', which are points of the center curve. We verify that B_c belongs to the center curve by noticing that the angles α_{31} and β_{31}, under which B_c sees the line segments $P_{23}P_{12}$ and $P_{34}P_{14}$, respectively, are equal. In comparing these angles they should both be measured in the same sense and should be the angles which carry the tails of the chordal vectors toward the heads (or vice versa, so long as we do both the same way).

(4) Similarly we verify that B_c' belongs to the center curve by noticing that angles α_{31}' and β_{31}' differ by 180 deg.

(5) As many additional points of the center curve as desired can be plotted by drawing additional pairs of circles with $P_{12}P_{23}$ and $P_{14}P_{34}$ as chords, always maintaining the ratio of radii the same as the ratio of chord lengths and keeping the circle centers on the same side of the chords as explained in (2) above.

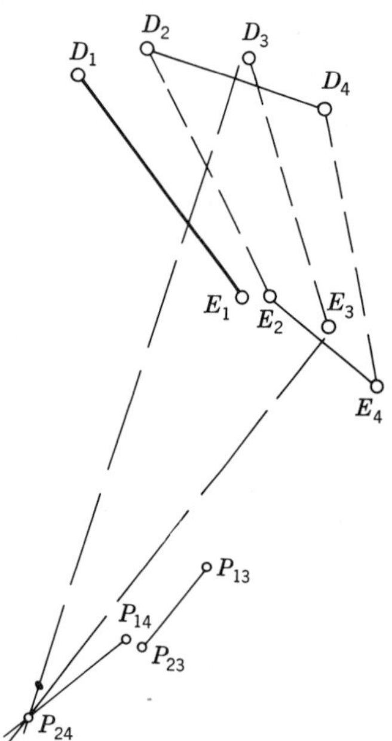

Fig. 8.25 A 4-bar linkage is to be designed to guide rigid body *DE* through the four positions shown. Construction is shown for finding one of the poles.

8.21 *Problem: design for guiding a body through four specified positions*

The line *DE* in Fig. 8.25 belongs to a body which is to be guided through four specified positions as described by D_1E_1, D_2E_2, D_3E_3, and D_4E_4. Guiding is to be accomplished by pivoting two cranks at suitable points A_c and B_c and pin jointing the cranks to corresponding points A and B of the moving body. A and B must, of course, be so chosen that they have their four positions on circles. Hence A_c and B_c must be points of the center curve. The design procedure is as follows.

(1) We need to plot a portion of the center curve. Hence we need one opposite pole quadrangle. We choose to use the quadrangle defined by the pairs of opposite poles P_{14}, P_{23} and P_{13}, P_{24}. Construction for finding one of these poles (P_{24}) is shown in Fig. 8.25.

(2) Having an opposite pole quadrangle, we can now plot points of the center curve by the method described in the previous article. Construction for finding one point is shown in Fig. 8.26.

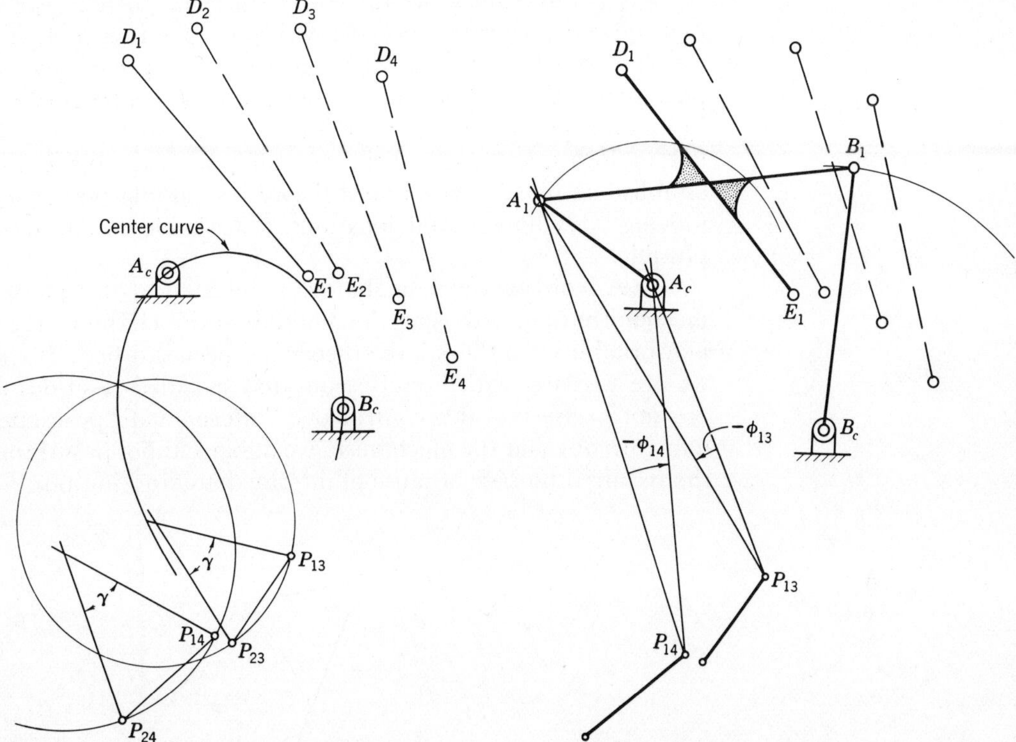

Fig. 8.26 Portion of the center curve plotted for the problem started in Fig. 8.25. A_c and B_c chosen as crank pivots.

Fig. 8.27 Completed design for the problem started in Fig. 8.25. Construction shows finding of A_1 corresponding to the chosen A_c.

(3) After plotting a portion of the center curve as shown in Fig. 8.26, we can make our choice of locations for the pivots A_c and B_c. Many different designs are possible. We illustrate only one.

(4) Having the pivots A_c and B_c, we must next find the pins A_1 and B_1. The problem here is identical with that of Art. 8.7. The construction for locating A_1 is shown in Fig. 8.27.

(5) The completed design is as shown in Fig. 8.27. We can check the accuracy of the design by turning the cranks and verifying that the moving body is guided to move through the four specified positions.

8.22 *Five positions*

A body can sometimes be guided through five specified positions by a pair of cranks. To do this requires finding two points belonging to the moving body and having their five positions on circles. If such points exist, the centers of the circles must lie at intersections of two center curves. For example, using the procedure of the previous article, we can plot the center curve associated with positions 1, 2, 3, 4. Then we can repeat, plotting the center curve associated with positions 1, 2, 3, 5. The intersections of the two center curves will be suitable points for the crank pivots. If two such intersections fall in locations where there are no practical objections to establishing fixed pivots, and if the corresponding points of the moving body have usable locations, a workable design may be possible.

A word of warning should be inserted at this point. A mechanism designed using the methods of this chapter may not be workable even though the theory has been satisfied. Because we are working with finitely separated specified positions and are not exercising any control over intermediate positions, it may turn out that the mechanism we design cannot pass through the required motion because of intermediate limiting positions.

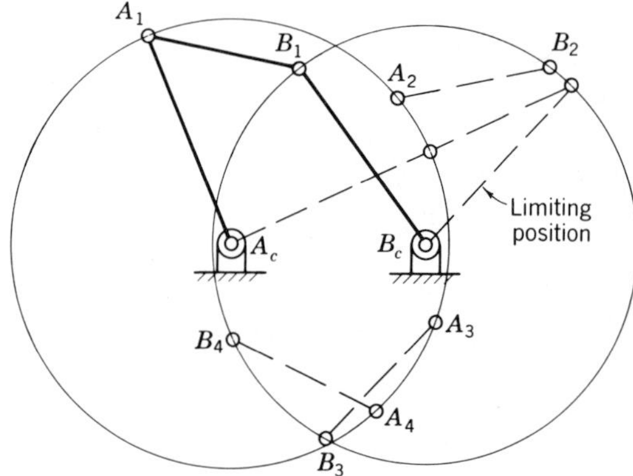

Fig. 8.28 A design which is theoretically correct by the methods of this chapter may not be workable because of intermediate limiting positions.

For example, Fig. 8.28 shows a 4-bar mechanism designed to guide the coupler through the four positions shown. Pivots A_c and B_c and pins A and B were properly selected in accordance with Art. 8.21. However, it is not a workable mechanism because it is impossible to move it from position 2 to position 3. When this situation arises, the designer must look for alternate solutions to his problem.

8.23 *Coordinated crank displacements: design problem*

So far in this chapter we have discussed the guiding of a moving body in plane motion with respect to a fixed body.

The same concepts apply to the coordination of crank angular displacements in the 4-bar mechanism, if we make use of the idea of inversion. We shall outline the procedure for such a design problem.

A 4-bar mechanism is to be designed such that, as the input crank rotates successively through three 30-deg. angles clockwise, the output crank will rotate successively in the opposite sense through angles of 15, 30, and 45 deg.

SOLUTION

(1) Figure 8.29(a). We choose locations O and Q for the pivots of the input and output cranks, respectively.

(2) We invert the mechanism, holding the input crank fixed and turning the frame OQ counterclockwise through three successive 30-deg. angles, thus defining Q_1, Q_2, Q_3, and Q_4, the four positions of Q relative to the input crank.

(3) We choose some line Q_1D_1 to be considered as attached to the output crank in position 1. The rotation angles of this line with respect to the input crank are to be as follows:

$$2\phi_{12} = 30 + 15 = 45 \text{ deg.}$$

$$2\phi_{13} = 60 + 45 = 105 \text{ deg.}$$

$$2\phi_{14} = 90 + 90 = 180 \text{ deg.}$$

Using this information, we can draw the other three positions of line QD.

(4) We now have a layout which enables us to find any of the poles for displacements of the output crank with respect

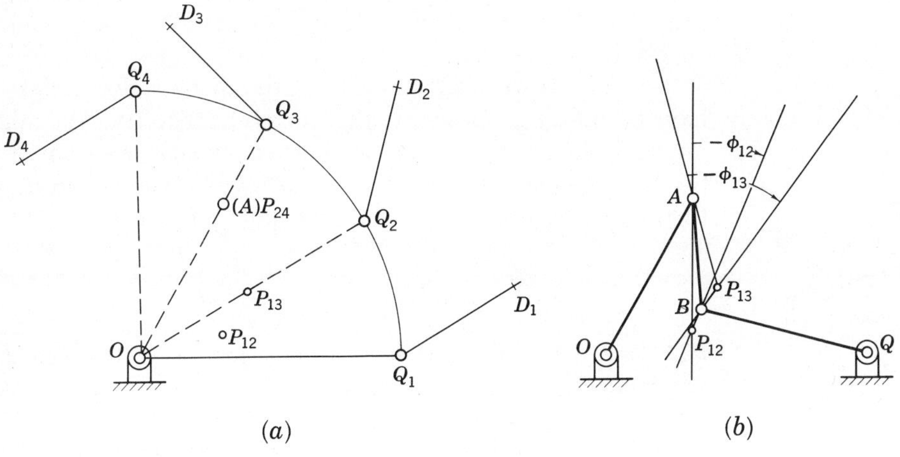

Fig. 8.29 Part of the graphical work in solving the problem of coordinating crank motions discussed in Art. 8.23. (a) Inverting the mechanism, establishing positions of one crank relative to the other. Poles P_{12}, P_{13}, and P_{24} are shown. (b) Design using location of P_{24} as crankpin A.

to the input crank. The figure shows the locations of poles P_{12}, P_{13}, and P_{24} (construction lines not shown).

(5) If we were to follow the general procedure, such as was done in Art. 8.21, we would find one more pole (P_{34}) to complete an opposite pole quadrangle and then proceed to plot a portion of the center curve for the motion of the output crank with respect to the input crank. However, this full procedure is not always necessary. It is frequently possible to take short cuts, one of which will be illustrated here.

(6) We know that the center curve, if plotted, would pass through all the poles. Hence, any one of the poles, P_{24} for example, might be a suitable location for the pin joint between the input crank and the connecting rod of the mechanism we are designing. We choose to try P_{24} as the location of this pin joint and will call it A.

(7) Since A belongs to the center curve for motion of the output crank with respect to the input crank, we can find the corresponding point of the output crank by the construction previously discussed. This is illustrated in Fig. 8.29(b). The point so located is called B.

(8) In the motion of the output crank with respect to the input crank, point B (considered as belonging to the output crank) will have its four positions located on a circle with A as center. Hence we may connect the two cranks by a rod AB as shown.

(9) To check the tentative design, we move the input crank through three successive 30-deg. angles and find the corresponding angles of rotation of the output crank, as shown in Fig. 8.30. The original layout from which these illustrations were taken was made on an $8\frac{1}{2} \times 11$ in. sheet with distance OQ less than 4 in. Even though this is too small a layout for precision work, the angular displacements of the output crank checked within 1 deg.

(10) If we are dissatisfied with our tentative design, we have an infinite number of other possibilities to try. We might, for example, try P_{34} as the location for pin A. Or we could use the more general procedure of plotting the center curve and then choosing a point other than a pole for pin A.

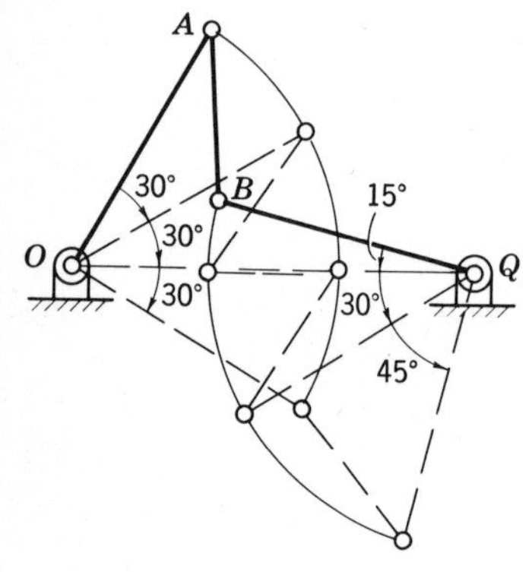

Fig. 8.30 Checking the mechanism as designed in Fig. 8.29.

Problems and Exercises

E8.1 (Fig. 8.31). A rigid body in plane motion is shown in three positions.

(a) Locate the poles and draw the pole triangle.

(b) Locate that point of the moving system which has its three positions on a circle arc about D_c as center.

(c) Determine the locus of points belonging to the moving system and having their three positions on straight lines.

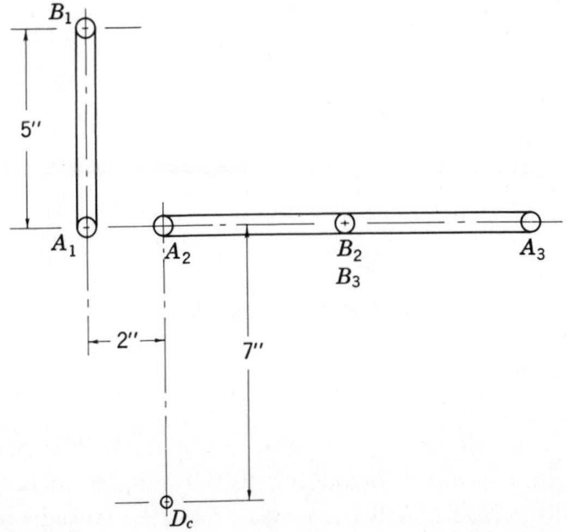

Fig. 8.31 Rigid body in three positions. Problem E8.1.

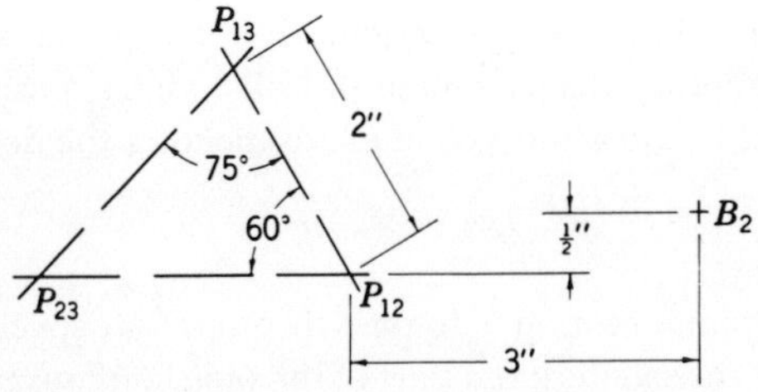

Fig. 8.32 Pole triangle for problem E8.2.

E8.2 (Fig. 8.32). The pole triangle is given for motion of a rigid body through three positions.

(a) Show the locations (in position 1) of all points having three positions on straight lines.

(b) Find B_1 and B_3 corresponding to the given B_2.

E8.3 (Fig. 8.33). Line g (shown as g_1 in position 1) belongs to a body moved through three positions, the pole triangle being as shown. Find g_2 and g_3 by the most direct construction you can devise.

E8.4 (Fig. 8.34.) The 4-bar mechanism shown is to be the initial drive for an intermittent motion mechanism. (Complete mechanism is to be of the type shown in part (b)). Pin C attached to the coupler of the 4-bar is to work in a straight slot of output link 5. Link 5 is to oscillate 20 $\pm$ 0.5 deg. and is to dwell while the crank rotates 90 deg. from the position shown. During the dwell period link 5 is not to move more than 0.5 deg. from its mean position for this period.

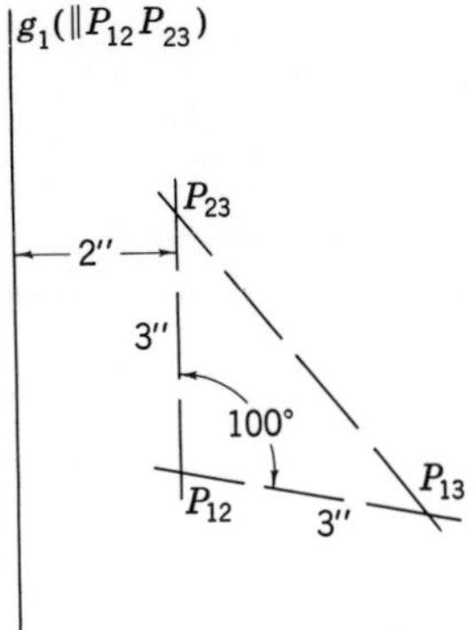

Fig. 8.33 Diagram for problem E8.3.

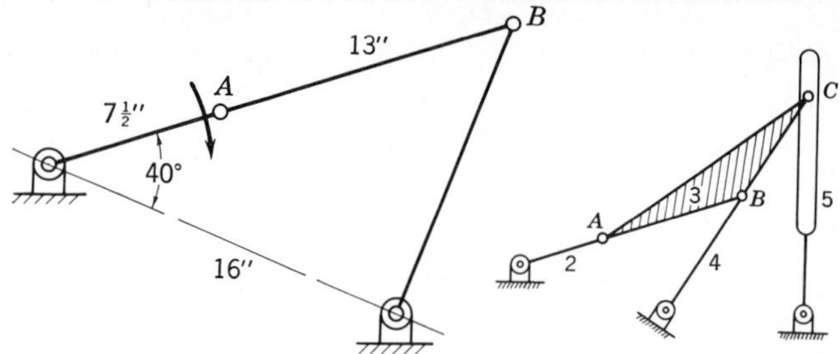

Fig. 8.34 Information for problem E8.4.

(a) Establish a tentative design for the mechanism. The major problem is to locate a point C belonging to the coupler such that during the "dwell" period C will travel very nearly a straight line. Try to find a point C by a 4-point approximation, i.e., use the methods of this chapter to locate a point such that four of its positions will fall on a straight line.

(b) When you have established your tentative design, make a diagram showing the angular displacement of link 5 versus position of the driving crank. How close did you come to meeting the design objectives?

E8.5 (Fig. 8.35)

(a) A rigid body in plane motion is to pass through four specified positions. The positions are such that a part of the pole configuration is as shown in Fig. 8.35(a). Determine the center curve.

(b) Same for Fig. 8.35(b).

E8.6 Three positions are specified for a body in plane motion. Positions 2 and 3 coincide. For two points, A and B, velocity directions are given in position 2 (or 3). Can the pole triangle be drawn? What is its nature?

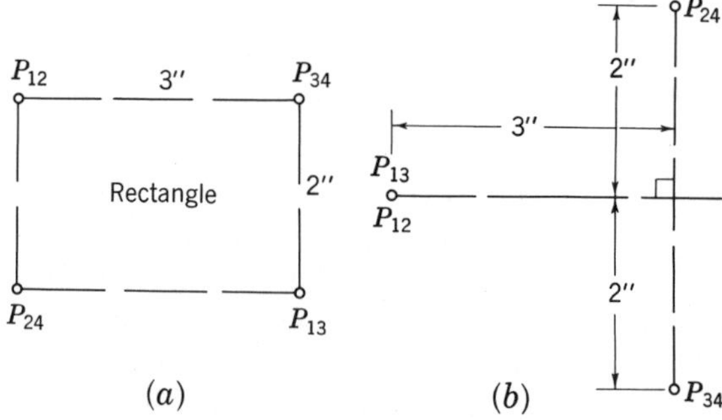

Fig. 8.35 Pole configurations for problem E8.5.

E8.7 Four positions are specified for a body in plane motion. Position 2 coincides with position 1. Position 4 coincides with position 3. For two points, A and B, velocity directions are specified in positions 1 (or 2) and 3 (or 4). Can the center curve be drawn? Analyze and discuss this situation.

E8.8 A 4-bar mechanism is required such that the two cranks will turn in opposite directions at nearly the same speed for a range of 90 deg. Design for four precision points in the input-output displacement relation. (Follow Art. 8.23.)

E8.9 Let three positions of a body in plane motion be specified. Assume the pole triangle to be given. Let D_k stand for a point whose three positions fall on a circle of a specified radius k.

(a) In general, for a given k, how many points D_k exist?

(b) Show how to find a point D_k.

(c) Show that the locus, in position 1, of all points D_k is a coupler curve. Show the 4-bar mechanism which generates the curve.

References

Items 1–8 are specifically mentioned in the text.

Items 9–15 are samples of current (not more than ten years old) periodical literature in English. If time permits, it is suggested that these (or others, as the instructor may suggest) be read in addition to the text.

Items 16–20 are useful reference books. Some of the topics treated briefly in this text are discussed more fully in these references.

1. HOLOWENKO, A. R., *Dynamics of Machinery,* John Wiley & Sons, New York, 1955, Chapter 9.

2. HARDING, B. L., *Proposed Standardized System for Notation and Classification of the Four-Bar Linkage,* ASME paper No. 57-F-28 (Photostatic copies available from Engineering Societies Library).

3. BEYER, R., *Technische Kinematik,* Johann Ambrosius Barth, Leipzig, 1931 (Lithoprint publication by J. W. Edwards, Ann Arbor, Mich., 1948), pp. 313–314.

4. HARTENBERG, R. S., and DENAVIT, J., "Cognate Linkages," *Machine Design,* April 16, 1959, pp. 149–152.

5. HRONES, J. A., and G. L. NELSON, *Analysis of the Four-Bar Linkage,* The Technology Press of M.I.T. and John Wiley & Sons, 1951.

6. FREUDENSTEIN, F., "Approximate Synthesis of Four-Bar Linkages," *Trans. ASME,* Aug. 1955, pp. 853–861.

7. FREUDENSTEIN, F., "Structural Error Analysis in Plane Kinematic Synthesis," *J. Eng. for Industry,* Feb., 1950, pp.15–22.

8. BURMESTER, L., *Lehrbuch der Kinematik,* A. Felix, Leipzig, 1888.

9. HALL, A. S., "Mechanisms and Their Classification," *Machine Design,* Dec., 1953, pp. 174-180.

Contains a little history and some personal opinions of the author.

10. GOODMAN, T. P., "An Indirect Method for Determining Accelerations in Complex Mechanisms," *Trans. ASME,* Nov., 1958, pp. 1676–1682.

Emphasizes the usefulness of mechanism inversions in kinematic analysis. Uses an indirect approach in which certain essentially geometric quantities are determined by kinematic analysis. Method is especially useful in studying compound mechanisms (mechanisms which are series or parallel combinations of simpler mechanisms). The effect on the compound mechanism of design changes in any of the component mechanisms can be studied without repeating the full analysis for the entire mechanism.

11. MODREY, J., "Analysis of Complex Kinematic Chains with Influence Coefficients," *J. of Appl. Mech.,* June 1959, pp. 184-188.

Prior to the publication of Modrey's paper it was possible to conceive complex kinematic chains which could not be analyzed by any of the usual textbook procedures. Modrey's technique resolves the analysis of highly complex mechanisms into a superposition of solutions of two or more simpler mechanisms.

12. PIKE, EUGENE W., THOMAS R. SILVERBERG and PHILIP T. NICKSON, "Linkage Layout," *Machine Design,* Nov. 1951, pp. 105–110, 194.

In addition to a very practical discussion of linkage layout methods, the article describes the use of "correcting cams" in conjunction with linkages.

13. HALL, A. S., Jr., and D. C. TAO, "Linkage Design—A Note on One Method," *Trans. ASME,* May 1954, pp. 633–637.

Svoboda (16) shows a method for improving the design of a linkage by making small changes in dimensions. His procedure makes use of coefficients of the form $\partial S/P_n$ where S is output displacement and P_n are dimensions of the linkage. Hall and Tao suggest a graphical vector procedure using velocity analysis for the determination of these coefficients. The graphical method may be particularly useful for linkages more complex than the 4-bar.

14. WOLFORD, J. C., "An Analytical Method for Locating the Burmester Points for Five Infinitesimally Separated Positions of the Coupler Plane of a Four-Bar Mechanism," *J. Appl. Mech.*, March 1960, pp. 182–186.

An extension of material of Chapter 6, this text. Burmester points are those points for which both first and second derivatives of path curvature, in the position considered, are zero.

15. DENAVIT, J., and R. S. HARTENBERG, "Approximate Synthesis of Spatial Linkages," *J. Appl. Mech.*, March 1960, pp. 201–206.

Following Freudenstein's lead for plane 4-bar mechanisms, the authors have gone on to show how and under what conditions the same ideas can be extended to spatial linkages. Design examples are worked out for three types of spatial 4-link mechanisms.

16. SVOBODA, A., *Computing Mechanisms and Linkages,* McGraw-Hill Book Company, New York, 1948.

An interesting book which probably sparked, or at least marked the beginning of, an upswing in interest in linkage synthesis following World War II. Pages 145–165 describe and show examples of what we have called the "overlay" method. Svoboda calls it the "geometric" method.

17. ROSENAUER, N., and A. H. WILLIS, *Kinematics of Mechanisms,* Associated General Publications, Sydney, Australia, 1953.

Devotes considerable space to the inflection circle, Euler-Savary equation, and related matters. (Also discusses constraint velocity, and acceleration analysis, and has a brief chapter on synthesis).

18. HAIN, K., *Angewandte Getriebelehre,* Hermann Schroedel, Hannover, Germany, 1952.

Hain and Beyer (19) are the leading German kinematicians. These two texts are among the best available in any language. Plans are currently under way for publishing English editions.

19. BEYER, R., *Kinematische Getriebesynthese,* Springer-Verlag, Berlin, 1953.

20. HUNT, K. H., *Mechanisms and Motion,* John Wiley & Sons, New York, 1959.

Chapter 7, *Space Mechanisms,* is a modest but well done introduction to the subject. Some consideration is given to space mechanisms in general. The important special cases of (a) the four-bar chain with hinged input and output and (b) the four-bar chain with hinged input and sliding output are studied in some detail.

INDEX

E

F

G

H

I